Animal production based on crop residu

Chinese experiences

FAO
ANIMAL
PRODUCTION
AND HEALTH
PAPER

149

C000155384

Edited by

Guo Tingshuang
Former Vice-Director
Animal Health and Production Bureau
Ministry of Agriculture
People's Republic of China

Manuel D. Sánchez
Animal Production Officer
FAO Animal Production and Health Division
Rome, Italy

and

Guo Pei Yu
Researcher
China Agricultural University
East Campus
People's Republic of China

FOOD AND AGRICULTURE ORGANIZATION OF THE UNITED NATIONS
Rome, 2002

ISBN 92-5-104639-5

Preface

It is a fact that China has to feed its large population, equivalent to 22 percent of the whole world, with only 7 percent of global farmland. How to feed over 1 300 million people is the central issue. Domestic experts in different research fields have proposed various solutions. One suggestion is to establish an intensive grain feeding system, based on local production and imports, as in most developed countries. But how can this be achieved? Let us analyse it. Since Mr. Deng Xiaoping established the so-called "productive related interest distributing system" in 1978, unprecedented production activity has developed in a vast area of the Chinese countryside. For the following six years (1979-1984), the annual increase in grain output (up to 17 million tonne) greatly surpassed population growth at the time. It was a successful policy. However, it was impossible to maintain that high pace relying only on that strategy. The increment fell to less than 4.5 million tonne per year for the next 16 years, despite high government inputs (finance, staff, etc.). Per capita grain availability also fell. Looking towards the future, it is possible that some increase in grain production will take place, but it will certainly be difficult to keep up with population growth.

Another proposal has been to meet the grain demand of China through imports, because it was known that subsidies had been offered by governments of major grain exporting countries. Thus, the greater the imports, the larger the subsidy. However, in contrast to Japan, Rep. of Korea and Singapore, China is a country with a huge population, and if its grain consumption approaches the USA level, there would be an annual demand of 80-100 million tonne of grain, nearly half of total world exports. Grain prices would skyrocket. In this case, what of subsidies? Further, it would be a serious risk for world food security to have China relying mostly on imports. That is the theme of Lester Brown's book *"Who will feed China?"*

Various pasture experts had another proposal. They hoped that grasslands, representing 40 percent of China's surface, would make a substantial contribution to food supply. This optimistic idea sounded reasonable, but the grasslands are suffering from serious degradation, desertification and alkalization processes, which cause serious concern. Everyone would like the government to devote more attention to the pasture problem: strengthening protective measures, reducing overgrazing and augmenting financial support. Then, after generations of hard work, it would be possible to recover the primary ecological system of grasslands. Most pasture experts tend to agree on this approach.

Since the development of an "intensive grain feeding system" is restricted by the lack of grain, and the potential of grassland is also a distant oasis that cannot quench present thirst, then the exploitation of various kinds of non-traditional feed resources is the most obvious way to resolve the issue. Crop residues are the most abundant and widespread of the non-traditional feed resources. Consequently, attention was directed to crop residues as the key missing feed in China.

In the mid-1980s, The MOA started studies on how to improve the efficiency of crop residue use. Soon after, with the support of agricultural colleges, research organizations and agricultural technical services in different areas, some small-scale trials were conducted. In 1987, financial support was offered by FAO and United Nations Development Programme (UNDP), and pilot projects of cattle feeding based on crop residues were conducted in provinces such as Hebei and Henan, in cooperation with the Ministry of Agriculture (MOA). A group of well-known international experts (including E.R. Orskov, F. Dolberg, F. Sundstol and P. Finlayson) visited China, and many Chinese technical officials and experts were sent abroad to study and train. Thus, the techniques for crop residue treatment and animal feeding matured gradually. Based on the success of the pilot projects, 14 experts – led by Guo Tingshuang and Ji Yilun – jointly submitted a written proposal to the Central Government "to develop animal production based on crop residues". Some high-level officials accepted this proposal. As noted earlier, there are diverse positions on this issue, both for and against. Pursuing the philosophy of respecting science and seeking the truth, the Bureau of Animal Production and Health (BAPH) of MOA organized a large-scale debate on this theme in 1991. The proposal for *Animal production based on crop residues* (APCR) than received preliminary acceptance. In 1992, a State Councillor, Mr Chen Junsheng, went to Zhoukou Prefecture in Henan Province to make an on-site observation, accompanied by the author. His report strongly confirmed the importance of APCR for national agriculture. Former Premier Li Peng praised it highly, calling it "such an exciting report". Subsequently, the State Council convened three national conferences within two years on APCR planning. A project demonstrating cattle raising with crop residues began in 1992. From then on, China's cattle sector emerged from a dormancy that had lasted several decades, and began a new period of rapid development. Within only three years, national beef output doubled. Since then, beef production has always led livestock sector growth. More than 90 percent of the beef expansion came from agricultural provinces. The correctness of the APCR policy was corroborated in practice.

Soon after, the State Council decided to expand the APCR rearing approach to include buffaloes, sheep, goats and dairy cattle. Thus far, the APCR has become part of government policy and is currently practised by numerous farmers. By 2000, 13 APCR demonstration prefectures and 380 demonstration counties had been established in the country. For the last nine years, the direct economic benefit of the APCR project has been calculated to exceed ¥ 70 000 million. In addition, the APCR project generated numerous social, agronomic and environmental benefits.

It was then considered necessary to summarize the practical experiences of APCR projects, and put them on a scientific or technical level for their further expansion. Thus, responding to the initiative of FAO, experts were organized to prepare a book to be published and distributed worldwide. Recognizing our limitations, there could be some involuntary mistakes. We kindly ask the readers of this book to point them out to us, so that they can be corrected in future editions.

Guo Tingshuang

Senior Engineer and Former Vice-Director
Bureau of Animal Production and Health,
Ministry of Agriculture, People's Republic of China
May, 2001

Acknowledgements

The book *Animal production based on crop residues – Chinese experiences* has finally been made available in English. Its publication has been possible thanks to thousands of technical staff who are working in the front line of animal production. They have been the ones who have popularized the new technology and who have accumulated the valuable experiences that are the source of this book. We express our deep appreciation to FAO for supporting the preparation of this book. In addition, the Bureau of Animal Production and Health, Department of International Cooperation (Ministry of Agriculture, PRC) and the China Agricultural University and their staff, contributed to the editing and offered technical and financial assistance. In the name of the group of authors, we thank them all.

We, the editors, also thank Professor Liu Xiangyang, Dr Wang Congling, Dr Kongyuan and Dr Zhou Jianqiang from China Agricultural University, and Mr Zhang Zhiqing from MOA, for their hard work in typing, drawing, proof reading and editing.

Guo Tingshuang
Manuel D. Sánchez
Guo Peiyu

May, 2001

Authors

Guo Tingshuang
Senior Engineer, Bureau of Animal Production and Health,
Ministry of Agriculture, 100026, Beijing, P.R. of China
E-mail: g_tingsh0028@sina.com

Manuel D. Sánchez
Animal Production Officer, Animal Production and Health Division,
Food and Agriculture Organization of the United Nations.
via delle Terme di Caracalla, 00100, Rome, Italy.
E-mail: manuel.sanchez@fao.org

Professor **Guo Peiyu**
Academy of Agricultural Engineering,
China Agricultural University, 100083, Beijing, P.R. of China
E-mail: guopy@bjaeu.edu.cn

Professor **Liu Jianxin**
College of Animal Sciences,
Zhejiang University. 310029, Hangzhou, P.R. of China.
E-mail: jxliu@dial.zju.edu.cn

Professor **Meng Qingxiang**
College of Animal Sciences and Technology
China Agricultural University, 100094, Beijing, P.R. of China
E-mail: qxmeng@mail.cau.edu.cn

Professor **Zhang Cungen**
Agricultural Economy Institute
China Academy of Agricultural Sciences, 100081, Beijing, P.R. of China
E-mail: Zhangcg@ihw.com.cn

Yang Zhenhai
Engineer, Director of Feed Division, Bureau of Animal Production and Health
Ministry of Agriculture, PRC. 100026, Beijing, P.R. of China
E-mail: xmjslch@agri.gov.cn

Zhang Zhishan
Engineer, Head of Grassland Division,
Bureau of Animal Production and Health
Ministry of Agriculture, PRC. 100026, Beijing, P.R. of China
E-mail: fanghb@agri.gov.cn

Professor **Han Lujia**
Director of Scientific Office
China Agricultural University, 100083, Beijing, P.R. of China
E-mail: ablate@163bj.com

Guo Jun
Technician, China National Animal Breeding Stock Import and Export Corporation
100026, Beijing, P.R. of China
E-mail: cabs@public3.bta.net.cn

Yan Qiaojuan
Lecturer, Academy of Agricultural Engineering
China Agricultural University, 100083, Beijing, P.R. of China
E-mail: yanqj@hotmail.com

CONTENTS

GLOSSARY OF ABBREVIATIONS AND UNITS xiv
CHAPTER 1 – INTRODUCTION 1
  A grain-saving strategy to develop animal production in China 1
  Arguments for a strategy for herbivores in China 4
  Methods for improving feeding value of crop residues 7
    Physical methods 8
    Biological methods 8
    Chemical methods 9
  Extension of the technology and herbivore development 11
    Sheep and goat raising 14
    Buffalo production 15
    Dairy production 15
    Deer rearing 16
  Economic, social, agronomic and environmental benefits
  of developing animal production based on crop residues 16
    APCR can save large amounts of feed grain. 16
    APCR favours agriculture 17
    Reducing environmental pollution 18
    Benefits in terms of meat availability 18
    Helping farmers to leave poverty 19
  The main successful extension experiences 20
    Highly relevant theme for national conditions 20
    Practical work was essential for rapid success 20
    Equal emphasis on all benefits 20
    A complete project 21
CHAPTER 2 – COMPOSITION, NUTRITIVE VALUE
AND UPGRADING OF CROP RESIDUES 22
  Introduction 23
  Botanical structure and cell wall chemical composition 24
    Botanical structure and digestion differences 24
    Chemical composition of cell walls 24
  Nutritive value of crop residues 27
  Factors affecting nutritive value of crop residues 29
    Plant factors 29
    Animal factors 31
    Environmental factors 32
  Improving feed value by processing or treatment 32
    Traditional processing and feeding methods 33
    Physical treatment 33

Chemical treatment 37
Biological approach 45
CHAPTER 3 – AMMONIATION OF CROP RESIDUES 51
Introduction 51
The principle and effects of straw ammoniation 52
Ammonia sources for straw ammoniation 52
Anhydrous ammonia 52
Urea 53
Ammonium bicarbonate 53
Aqueous ammonia 54
Other sources 54
Methods for ammonia treatment of straw 54
Stack method 54
Silo or bunker method 60
Oven method 63
Other options 64
Factors influencing effectiveness of ammoniation 64
Ammonia dosage 64
Moisture content of straw 65
Temperature and treatment time 67
Quality of material being treated 67
Pressure 68
Quality evaluation of ammoniated straw 68
Sensory evaluation 68
Chemical analysis 68
Biological tests 69
Animal experiments with ammoniated straw 71
Feeding experiments with beef cattle 71
Feeding dairy cows 75
Feeding sheep 76
CHAPTER 4 – ENSILING CROP RESIDUES 79
Types of silos 80
Tower silo 80
Cellar silo 80
Trench silo 80
Stack silo 80
Plastic silo 83
Silage making 83
Control of moisture content in raw materials 83
Chopping, compaction and sealing 84
Factors influencing silage quality 85
Silage additives 86
Bacterial cultures 87

Chapter 1

Introduction

**Guo Tingshuang and
Yang Zhenhai**
Ministry of Agriculture

A GRAIN-SAVING STRATEGY TO DEVELOP ANIMAL PRODUCTION IN CHINA

Since the "Reform and Opening-up" of 1978, animal production in China has grown steadily year by year. In 1999, total meat output reached 59.5 million tonne and egg output 21.3 million tonne, both ranked first in the world. For the ten years after 1978, China represented nearly half the total global annual increase in meat and egg production. Even though population increased continuously, per capita meat, egg and milk production rose with an ample margin. Between 1949 and 1979, annual per capita meat consumption amounted to less than 5 kg, but by the end of the 1990s it had increased by 39 kg of meat per capita (Figure 1-1).

Although the livestock sector has shown remarkable achievements in the past two decades, there are also hidden worries. One of the main concerns is the lack of feed grain. Cereal production is a weak link in the national economy. During the last decade, grain output growth could not keep up with the increase in population, and at the same time arable area has been constantly reduced. Therefore, the future of grain supply may be very serious. One or two exceptional harvest years can not fundamentally change this situation. According to researchers, per capita grain-equivalent consumption in some metropolises such as Beijing, Shanghai, Tianjin, Shenyang, Guangzhou, etc. has already exceeded 400 kg. In Beijing, direct grain consumption was only 120 kg in 1989, but consumption of meat, eggs and milk required the equivalent of 400 kg extra, bring the total to more than 520 kg of grain-equivalent per capita. Grain production per capita in China was only 389 kg in 1999. If the consumption level of meat, eggs and milk in the whole of China had reached by 2000 that of Beijing in 1989, 182 million tonne of additional grain would have been necessary. During the past decade, net increase in grain yield was only 80 million tonne. Therefore, if the livestock sector were to depend mostly on grain, its development would inevitably be seriously restricted.

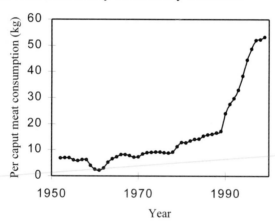

Figure 1-1. Development of per capita meat consumption in China

The dependency of the animal industry on grain relates to its structure. Over the past decades, due to state promotion, swine rearing developed rapidly and became the largest animal sector in the country. In 1978, pork represented more than 94 percent of total meat output. Since the "Reform and Opening-up," this situation has gradually changed. The proportion of poultry, beef and mutton increased yearly, while that of pork fell. Currently, pork still represents 67 percent of total consumption, but poultry, beef and mutton now contribute 20, 7.8 and 4 percent, respectively. Compared with world data (Table 1-1), China is the leader in pork production, with 50 percent, but only produces 10 percent of beef. Generally speaking, feed conversion efficiency in swine is less than for poultry. On this basis, suitably limiting swine rearing and promoting poultry production ought to be a rational strategy. In the past 20 years, great effort was made to develop poultry production, with significant progress made. The proportion of poultry meat rose from 8.6 to 20 percent, and its growth is expected to continue. However, both swine and poultry require concentrates as their main feed and therefore they will be inevitably restricted by grain shortages. The rearing of herbivores without grain, but with small quantities of oil cake, should show considerable development. Adhering to a grain-saving strategy for the industry, the future of China's livestock development can be firmly based on stable feed resources, less susceptible to grain production fluctuations.

Table 1-1. Meat distribution in the world and in China in 1998 (in percent)

	Beef	Mutton	Pork	Poultry meat	Other
World	26.2	5.2	38.9	27.9	1.8
China	7.9	4.0	67.0	20.1	1.1

The well-known economist, Mr Yu Guangyuan, considered that the grain problem in China was essentially a feed issue. As indicated before, per capita grain output is 389 kg, more than enough to cover direct food grain needs (230 kg each), but not enough for feed. It is therefore clear that establishing a grain-saving strategy in the animal sector could help alleviate the problem. Certainly, the significance of this ought not to be underestimated. India, also a developing country with large population and limited farmland, faces a similar situation. Per capita grain yield is slightly more than one half of China's, but India does not need to import grain, because they have adopted a grain-saving approach to feeding livestock. From Figure 1-2 it can be observed that pursuing the USA way, in other words, devoting 70 percent of grain production to animal feeds, over half of the Chinese population would have no food grain. But following India's example, using only 2 percent of grain as feed, China's grain is not only sufficient, but there would be a huge surplus. Of course, it is not advocated to imitate India, but the experience can certainly be a valid reference to consider for the Chinese case.

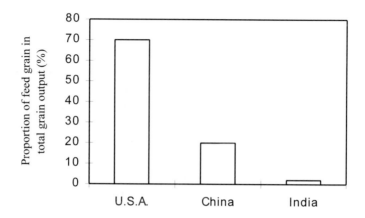

Figure 1-2. Feed grain as a proportion of total grain output

ARGUMENTS FOR A STRATEGY FOR HERBIVORES IN CHINA

Chinese experts have had active debates for a while on how best to raise domestic herbivores. Whenever mentioning their development, people always think of the vast northern prairie. The verse

> "the blue sky, the boundless grassland,
> while wind blows, grass, cattle and sheep can be found"

is very well known. The northern prairie, with nearly 300 million ha, almost three times the total farming area of the country, has been the basis of traditional herbivore production. In the past several thousand years, Inner Mongolia, Xinjiang, Qinghai and Tibet have been the main regions for herbivore production. For several decades, exploitative use (mainly overgrazing and excessive land conversion of natural pasture to arable) has caused serious deterioration in the northern prairie. Consequently, forage output has declined by 30-50 percent since the 1950s. Meanwhile, animal numbers increased after the founding of People's Republic of China in 1949. The current carrying capacity of the northern prairie for existing animals is insufficient, so how can anyone talk about livestock development there? A fundamental ecological recovery of the northern prairie would require significant investments and the efforts of several generations. Certainly, one could not get the desired result in a short period. Therefore, the development of herbivore production can not be expected from grasslands.

The above argument has been disputed. Someone said that over the past several decades people have just extracted products from the prairie, with little input. The State provided under one yuan (US$ 1 = ¥ 8.27) per *mu* (1/15 ha) of grassland. With sufficient investment to favourably recover the prairie ecology, the huge potential of the grasslands could be exploited for livestock. In the future, the government would need to greatly increase investment in grasslands. However, as China is a developing country, it is unrealistic to expect large investments for this purpose. Recovering the prairies, constructing a whole system with water, grass, forest, machinery and roads, would need at least ¥ 300/*mu*, implying the sum of ¥ 10^{12} for the 3 300 million *mu* of utilizable grassland – an astronomical figure! The current State annual budget for livestock is only several hundred million *yuan*. If this funding level were devoted solely to grassland reconstruction, a thousand years would be needed. However, this simplistic analysis clearly demonstrates that large investment for prairie rehabilitation is not a viable option. The current urgent issue is to prevent further grassland deterioration. Grasslands must recover gradually, with reasonable inputs.

If natural grassland is not available, what about artificial pastures? There have been suggestions that China should follow New Zealand's approach, and rely on planted grass, with almost no concentrates. The prosperous livestock sector brought New Zealand to its developed status. South China, with over one thousand million *mu* of grassy hills and slopes, and favourable water and climatic resources, better than in the northern prairie, could be transformed into several New Zealands. This proposal has a certain validity, since the southern grassy hills and slopes clearly have an enormous potential. In certain locations, artificial grasslands could be established, but this approach, as a general strategy, is not advisable. This is because the available farmland must be used for food crops, rather than for forage, so as to feed the huge population. New Zealand uses 270 000 km² (twice Jiangsu Province) to feed 3.3 million people ad to export (Jiangsu Province has over 50 million). Going the New Zealand way, China's 9.6 million km² could only feed 120 million people. And how to feed the rest, over 1 000 million people?

If the grassland strategy for livestock development is not feasible, then what is the option? Extensive research and vast demonstrations have shown that rural areas have an extraordinary potential for herbivore production. In China, there is an annual production of 500 million tonne of grain and 600 million tonne of crop residues (Table 1-2), the latter equivalent to almost fifty times the hay from the northern prairie. Furthermore, the ample supplies of cottonseed cake, rapeseed cake and brans can be used as inexpensive concentrates. Relying on abundant roughage and concentrates, coupled with a benign climate and sufficient qualified staff, the rural areas are rapidly developing and becoming the main source for herbivore products in China. The comparison between Inner Mongolia and Henan Provinces clearly illustrates this. In 1982, Henan Province had 55 000 head of cattle, one sixth of Inner Mongolia. Four years later, Henan Province had surpassed Inner Mongolia, and in 1999 it produced 5 518 million head of cattle, over four times that of Inner Mongolia (Figure 1-3).

Table 1-2. Amounts of various crop residues in 1993 ('000 tonne)

Crop residue	Amount	Crop residue	Amount
Rice straw	187 913	Peanut vine	6 623
Wheat straw	109 292	Rape stalks	20 874
Maize stover	155 152	Sugar cane tops	14 405
Millet straw	6 390	Sesame stalks	299
Sorghum stubble	10 228	Sunflower stalks	803
Soybean straw	14 985	Cotton leaves	2 705
Coarse grain straw	19 588	Edible sesame stalks	1 600
Sweet potato vine	24 359	**Total**	575 215

SOURCE: Data from Non-conventional Feed Development and Application Task Team (Agricultural Science Academy of China, 1993).
NOTE: In 1993, grain output was 450 million tonne. Now it is 500 million tonne, so the amount of crop residues should be over 600 million tonne

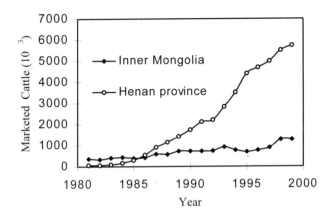

Figure 1-3. Cattle production development in Henan and Inner Mongolia Provinces

Currently, the agricultural areas of the Central Plain provinces of Shandong, Henan, Anhui and Hebei have already become the leading beef and mutton producers in the country, more than Inner Mongolia, Xinjiang, Qinghai and Tibet Provinces, the largest pastoral zones. Apart from these four agricultural provinces, many other areas have similar conditions, and with a suitable approach, these also have the production potential of the Central Plain provinces, and could quickly become beef cattle zones or goat and sheep belts.

It is clear that agricultural areas have an immense potential for herbivore production. This approach can be termed animal production based on crop residues. The fact that livestock production based on crop residues is advocated does seem to ignore pasture production. Both are very important and mutually complementary. Currently, special emphasis is given to livestock in crop areas because it had been neglected in the past, with its enormous potential ignored.

The debate on herbivore development strategies has so far concluded that livestock based on crop residues is the most viable for China. The agricultural areas should be the main source for herbivore production.

METHODS FOR IMPROVING THE FEEDING VALUE OF CROP RESIDUES

Crop residues are the main agricultural by-products in the countryside. Since ancient times, Chinese farmers have traditionally fed crop residues to herbivores. From the 600 million tonne of crop residues produced at present, about a third is used as feed. Most of this was untreated, and thus with low digestibility, low crude protein (CP) content and poor palatability, and so intake has been low. Untreated residues can barely satisfy maintenance requirements, and, as a result, animal performance is modest. For the past twenty years, scientists and technicians in China have studied and tested several methods for improving the feeding value of crop residues, and these are summarized here.

Physical methods

Chopping straw and stubble to 1 cm, or a little longer, before feeding is practised widely in the north. There is a saying among farmers "chopping hay to one inch, fattening can be done without concentrate." Scientific tests have shown that chopping does not improve straw digestibility, but it increases intake to a certain degree and reduces feed waste. It is a simple and effective method, with ample practical application. Grinding straw does not improve digestibility either, it just wastes energy in vain. However, ground straw easily mixes with other feed components. It is widely applied in feedlot fattening.

Apart from chopping and grinding, others have tried steaming, irradiation treatment, etc., as means to improve the feeding value of crop residues. There has been some progress, but it has not reached the practical application stage. There is also the so-called "salting" method, in which chopped straw is soaked in a dilute salt solution before feeding. Although this method has not been scientifically tested, many farmers in northeast and north China practise it, considering it effective.

Biological methods

The purpose is to allow microbes to degrade cellulose or lignin in straw as a means to improve its nutritive value. In the past half century, many local and foreign scientists have conducted research on this approach, but until now the ideal method has not been found. In the early 1990s, the "micro-storage" technology became popular. MOA found that this technology did not improve straw digestibility, but the treatment resulted in a product with a fragrance similar to wine, which improved palatability and intake. Thereby farmers welcomed it, and it was rapidly popularized.

Up to now, silage is still the most important microbial treatment method in practical application. In 1999, silage making surpassed the 100 million tonne level nationally, but its main limitation is that at best it can preserve the nutrients contained in green straw. Silage making is very widely used.

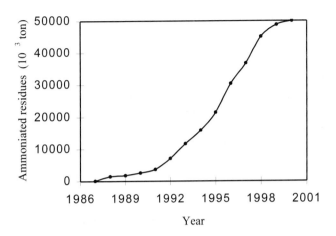

Figure 1-5. Ammoniation of crop residues in China in recent years

Utilizing crop residues as the feed base to develop cattle raising has been the main achievement of APCR. However, it has gone well beyond cattle. The following sections describe other important accomplishments.

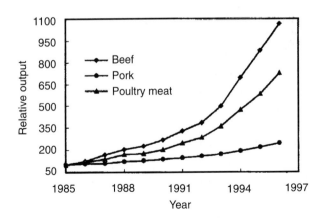

Figure 1-6. Growth curves for production of various meats (1985 as 100%)

Sheep and goat raising

Since the "Reform and Opening-up," along with economic growth and livelihood improvement, mutton demand and price have increased. In contrast, sheep and goat production were in decline at one time. Research demonstrated that due to grassland deterioration and forage shortage, sheep and goat raising was constrained in agricultural areas. At the same time, grazing sheep and goats also conflicted with forestry, and mountain areas were closed for forest protection. This led to a lack of grazing land for sheep and goats, limiting production. Feed trials indicated that sheep and goats are similar to cattle in digesting crop residues. If the modality of feeding sheep and goats were changed from grazing to use of crop residues, silage and ammoniated stalks, properly supplemented with concentrates, a significant development in sheep and goat production could be expected. In 1993, based on our proposal, the State Council decided to include sheep and goat raising with crop residues in the State Agricultural Comprehensive Development Programme (SACDP). From that point, sheep and goat production began a period of fast development. In 1999, domestic mutton output reached 2 513 million tonne, over double the figure before project start in 1991, with 80 percent coming from the agricultural areas.

Buffalo production

There are over 20 million buffaloes in China, the second largest population in the world. Buffaloes are mainly used for traction, and in most regions of China. With agricultural mechanization, the role of buffaloes for draught weakens yearly. If an alternative use of buffalo for milk and meat is not found, recession in the buffalo population will be unavoidable. Furthermore, buffalo rearing in south China is based on grazing, and weight loss is serious due to insufficient grass. Besides, grazing land has been reduced due to forest protection in recent years. Without a change in raising modality, buffalo will be certainly difficult to develop.

Trials have shown that buffaloes digest crop residues very well, and considering that their milk and dairy products are much appreciated and demanded in Europe, development based on ammoniated stalks could have export opportunities. Buffalo meat is also well accepted, not only in Guangdong and Guangxi, but also in Hong Kong and Macao. The Yellow cattle are very small in south China, and there is a saying "a shoulder pole can carry two cattle." If cattle of this region are not improved, it will be hard to meet export standards for size. In contrast, buffaloes can easily meet these size requirements (for Hong Kong and Macao) without improvement. Both buffalo meat and milk are excellent, and buffaloes are also suitable for roughage-based feeding, so there is a bright prospect for them. The State has already established buffalo demonstration counties in Guangxi Autonomous Region. Dairy and meat buffalo production units will appear in south China in the coming years.

Dairy production
The possibility of developing dairy production in agricultural areas is also very large. Except in Heilongjiang Province, the country's dairy cows are mainly around large- or medium-sized cities. The shortage of forage in these areas has already become one of most important limiting factors restricting production. Large amounts of hay are bought annually for the more than 60 000 dairy cows of Beijing, from as far away as the northeastern regions, at a cost of almost ¥ 10 million. In recent years, tests carried by the Beijing Dairy Cow Centre substantiated that hay could be substituted, partly or totally, by ammoniated residues. If this change occurs in practise, not only would feed costs be sharply reduced, but also transportation shortages alleviated. There is therefore a solution to the dairy cow roughage supply problem in urban areas. Per capita milk consumption in China is less than 7 kg, far below 10 percent of the world's mean. The domestic market for dairy products is very large indeed. Applying APCR for dairy cattle can greatly increase milk production. China produced 8 069 million tonne of milk in 1999, 154 percent more than in 1991.

Deer rearing
With higher living standards, demand for a variety of delicacies has increased in recent years, and so deer production also has bright prospects. In New Zealand, deer are raised just like sheep. Deer graze pastures all year round, without special care. During the Qing Dynasty, royal deer gardens were set up in the northeastern provinces, so deer husbandry in China is more than a century old, with animals tamer than those in New Zealand. Implementing deer raising based on crop residues can benefit the deer sector. In recent years, deer farms have been established in the Guangdong Leizhou Peninsula. Despite differences in climate and feed compared to the northeast, deer do very well. Velvet antler quality is also quite good. This indicates that trying silage and ammoniated residues as the basic feed to develop deer is well justified.

ECONOMIC, SOCIAL, AGRONOMIC AND ENVIRONMENTAL BENEFITS OF DEVELOPING ANIMAL PRODUCTION BASED ON CROP RESIDUES

The importance of APCR goes beyond the animal industry itself. Its development not only implies significant economic benefits, but also results in attractive social and environmental benefits. These are summarized below.

APCR can save large amounts of feed grain.

There were 117 million tonne of silage made and 50 million tonne of crop residues ammoniated in China in 1992. This represented grain feed savings of over 37.7 million tonne (using the "oat unit" for conversion). Currently, 200 million tonne of treated crop residues and 111 million tonne of untreated crop residues are being used as feed in the country, saving the equivalent of 22 million tonne of feed grain. The utilization of crop residues could be doubled within ten years, and, in this case, annual grain savings would increase to 120 million tonne, meeting 80 percent of grain demand. The significance of this can not really be underestimated.

APCR favours agriculture

In the past decade, increasing amounts of chemical fertilizer have been applied to land as one of main methods to raise grain yields. However, this practice raises costs, worsens soil condition and causes environment pollution. The utilization efficiency of chemical fertilizer in China is only 30 percent. Nearly 70 percent flows into rivers, lakes and sea. This has caused nutrient enrichment of water bodies and sporadic coastal "red tides".

In recent years, the Agricultural Department has strongly encouraged the direct return of crop residues to farmland to increase fertility, organic matter content and to raise the soil's capacity to conserve water and nutrients. However, direct application of crop residues to farmland is expensive and potentially harmful to germination of the following crop. In addition, this practice might not help to reduce crop diseases and pests. Because of these concerns and despite strong promotion, the direct return of residues to agricultural land remains very limited.

When crop residues pass through the animal digestive system and are returned to farmland as manure, the above worries cease. It has been already demonstrated that silage (anaerobic fermentation) and ammoniation reduce harmful microbes, pests and weed seeds. In addition, digestion of crop residues

Table 2-5. Composition and *in vitro* DM digestibility of wheat and rice straw fractions

Fraction	n	Chemical composition (% of DM)					IVOMD (%)
		NDF	ADF	CEL	HC	ADL	
Wheat straw							
Whole plant[1]	16	79.1	54.9	43.2	24.2	7.9	43.0
Stem	16	87.1	55.1	46.4	32.1	8.6	24.8
Leaf sheath	16	82.4	56.0	49.1	26.4	7.0	44.5
Leaf blade	16	71.6	52.8	46.9	18.8	5.9	61.5
Rice straw							
Whole plant[1]	16	67.2	46.3	33.8	20.9	5.2	35.7
Stem	16	61.1	43.6	35.4	21.3	4.5	51.8
Leaf sheath	16	71.9	48.4	34.6	23.5	5.5	25.4
Leaf blade	16	61.1	39.8	25.5	21.2	5.5	33.4

SOURCE: Xing Tingxian (1995).

KEY: n = number of replicates; NDF = neutral detergent fibre; ADF = acid detergent fibre; CEL = cellulose; HC = hemicellulose; ADL = acid detergent lignin; IVOMD = *in vitro* organic matter digestibility.

NOTE: (1) Without grain.

Animal factors

Little information is available about animal factors that influence the nutritive value of crop residues. Farmers in China have long known that different breeds and types of animals use crop residues with various efficiencies. Cattle, which retain fibrous matter in the rumen slightly longer than sheep or goats, presumably have an advantage with lower quality crop residues.

Cross-bred Brahman (*Bos indicus*) steers, when fed hay with 730 g/kg NDF, digested more NDF in the rumen and had longer ruminal retention time for lignin than did Hereford (*B. taurus*) steers (Kennedy, 1982). With increasing popularization of cross-breeding techniques in China, farmers noted that, on a high concentrate diet basis, hybrid beef steers have much better growth performance than do native breeds; in contrast, on a low-quality fibrous feed (e.g. crop residues), the contrary was observed. Although the exact mechanism of this difference in animal performance between hybrid and native breeds is unclear, an inherent difference in food intake and digestion capacity may be responsible.

Environmental factors

Some environmental factors, including location, climate, soil fertility and soil type, seem to influence the nutritive value of crop residues. Recent studies (Xing Tingxian, 1995) have indicated that there can be significant differences in chemical composition and digestibility of crop residues grown on different soil types (Table 2-6). Irrespective of crop cultivar, straw from wheat grown in the so-called tide soils (alluvial soils with diurnal variation in groundwater level) had considerably higher CP content and lower fibre (NDF, ADF and ADL) content than straw from drab soils (cinammon soils of forest origin). These are probably the cause of digestibility differences.

Table 2-6. Composition and *in vitro* DM digestibility of wheat straw by soil type

Parameter	Soil type	Wheat cultivar		
		No.3039	Bao feng	ZY No.1
CP	Tide soil	6.4	4.8	4.6
	Drab soil	3.7	3.3	3.3
NDF	Tide soil	64.4	71.2	58.5
	Drab soil	69.7	74.8	75.9
ADF	Tide soil	48.6	57.3	45.7
	Drab soil	58.4	55.1	64.6
ADL	Tide soil	7.4	8.3	6.2
	Drab soil	7.4	8.5	9.6
IVDMD	Tide soil	48.6	49.4	54.9
	Drab soil	53.6	45.3	33.8

SOURCE: Xing Tingxian, 1995.

KEY: CP = crude protein; NDF = neutral detergent fibre; ADF = acid detergent fibre; ADL = acid detergent lignin; IVDMD = *in vitro* DM digestibility.

IMPROVING FEED VALUE BY PROCESSING OR TREATMENT

Ruminants despite their unique and highly efficient digestive system, are not able to extract sufficient energy to grow and produce milk from low quality or highly lignified residues. These must be properly processed or treated in some way to make them useful for production.

Traditional processing and feeding methods

Historically, many fibrous crop by-products have been used as energy sources for ruminants in China. More than 1 000 years ago, during the Song Dynasty, Chen Fu in his *Nong Shu Book* [Agriculture Encyclopaedia] described the following method of processing and feeding crop residues:

> "Mix finely chopped straw with wheat or millet bran and beans, slightly soak them with water, and then feed animals *ad libitum*."

and there is a farmers' proverb:

> "chopping hay to one inch, fattening can be done without concentrate".

These ancient processing and feeding methods include particle reduction and reconstitution of roughage, and are still included in university textbooks and scientific publications. Chopping and water soaking are popular practices for crop residue feeding throughout the country. Although they do not always result in consistent improvements in animal performance, they definitely result in reduced diet wastage and diet selection (Xiong, 1986).

A method called *Jiegan Nian Qing* (crushing freshly cut alfalfa with straw) has been widely used in the southern part of Shanxi Province. A thick layer (about 30 cm) of wheat or rice straw is spread on a flat threshing ground. A layer of freshly cut alfalfa (about 30 cm thick) is put on top, followed by another layer of straw. A heavy stone roller is passed over the layers, squeezing out the alfalfa juice, which is absorbed by the straw. The alfalfa treated in this way can be dried much faster, with minimum leaf loss, and at the same time, the alfalfa juice absorbed by the straw enhances the straw feed value. This method is very useful in those areas where alfalfa drying is difficult.

Physical treatment

Numerous physical processing techniques to enhance the utilization of crop residues by ruminants have been used, with varying degrees of success. In this section, the more common methods – including grinding and pelleting, irradiation and steam treatment – will be briefly reviewed as they relate to crop residue utilization in China.

Grinding and pelleting

The most studied physical treatments for enhancing crop residue use by ruminants are grinding and pelleting. Grinding, or fine chopping, decreases particle size, increases surface area and bulk density of both leaf and stem fractions, and hence raises rumen microbial accessibility or feed intake. The increase in intake due to grinding is generally higher with low quality than with high quality residues, and with small and young animals rather than with older and larger animals. The critical feed particle size to exit the rumen is smaller in sheep than in adult cattle and therefore a greater degree of grinding is necessary before they leave the rumen. Screen sizes for hammer mill grinding in China range from 2.5 mm to 25 mm. Considering differences in intake between animal species and the energy expenditure for grinding, Xiong (1986) recommended 6 mm for sheep and 12 mm for cattle as the appropriate screen sizes for hammer mills.

Ground crop residues are often pelleted or cubed before feeding. Benefits derived from pelleting include a further increase in density, decreased dustiness and easier handling. However, DM digestibility of pelleted straws is depressed relative to the long or chopped forms, primarily due to faster passage rate. Pelleting usually augments straw intake due to quicker passage, which can offset the negative effect from decreased digestibility. Therefore, the net benefit of feeding pelleted crop residues in practice is increased energy intake and animal performance. In dairy cows, fine grinding and pelleting of forages can dramatically reduce rumination and rumen digestion times. Consequently, saliva production is reduced and the rumen fermentation pattern is altered, together with reduction in acetate/propionate ratio. This is believed to be the reason for the milk fat reduction with ground and pelleted forages.

Few studies have been conducted to assess the feeding value of ground and pelleted crop residues in China. Fu *et al.* (1991) studied the response of lamb growth performance to ground and pelleted maize stover. Compared with coarse grinding of maize stover (through a 25-mm screen), processing with fine grinding (through an 8-mm screen) followed by pelleting increased feed intake by half (1 098 g vs 728 g DM) and daily gain by 129 percent (148 g vs 65 g), and reduced the feed/gain ratio by 34.1 percent (7.4 vs 11.3).

Kneading

As milk fat can be lowered with finely ground or pelleted straws, the development of another physical processing method was necessary. Recently, a novel method for processing crop residue using a kneading machine has been reported (Gao Zhenjiang *et al.*, 1994). When fibrous crop residues enter the machine, they are kneaded into threadlike fibres or hairs with no apparent stem internode structure. Kneading extensively destroys the rigid structure and thus significantly increases voluntary intake. Unlike other physical processing, such as grinding or pelleting, rubbing of crop residues produces long threadlike fibres (usually 8-12 cm long), and therefore should not affect milk fat content. Compared to chopping, kneading requires higher energy expenditure.

Several studies have been conducted to compare kneading with traditional chopping. Sun Zhongyin *et al.* (1991) reported that dairy cows fed with scrubbed soybean residue had higher dietary DM intake and milk production than with untreated residue. A similar result with kneaded maize stover fed to dairy cows was reported by Zhao Xiyou and Sun Qinglin (1992). Kneading treatment is becoming popular in China.

Irradiation

Irradiation treatment of lignocellulosic materials to improve the utilization of cell wall polysaccharides dates back to the work of Lawton *et al.* (1951). They found that when basswood was irradiated with high velocity electrons, rumen bacteria fermentation was increased. Electron irradiation of straw can also increase polysaccharide digestibility by ruminal micro-organisms. Based on volatile fatty acid (VFA) production during fermentation, the optimum dose appears to be at 2.5 ¥ 10^8 rad. *In vitro* DM disappearance increased with irradiation dosage up to 10^8 rad (Pritchard *et al.*, 1962).

Several studies on irradiation of crop residues for increasing their nutritive value have been conducted in China. Meng Qingxiang and Xiong Yiqiang (1990) treated wheat straw with a combination of g-rays from a cobalt-60 source and NH_3 (3 percent of DM) or NH_3 (1 percent) plus CaOH (5 percent of DM) at different moisture levels. They found that irradiation doses (2 ¥ 10^5, 2 ¥ 10^6 or 2 ¥ 10^7 rad) had a significant interaction with the moisture level (20, 40 or 60 percent for ammoniation, and 40, 50 or 60 percent for NH_3 + CaOH). On either chemical treatment, as irradiation and moisture level increased, *in situ* DM disappearance (ISDMD) increased and NDF content diminished dramatically. These results suggest that responses to irradiation at a lower dosage can be compensated by higher moisture levels. In another study, Gu Chuipeng *et al.* (1988b) found lower contents of fibrous fractions (NDF, ADF and lignin) and elevated ISDMD with irradiation of rice straw. When straw was irradiated at dosage of 0, 5 ¥ 10^6, 10^7, 5 ¥ 10^7 and 10^8 rad, the ISDMD were 54.0, 54.7, 57.5, 71.0 and 75.5 percent, respectively. Treatment of rice straw with a combination of electron irradiation and NaOH also resulted in a considerable higher glucose release (Lu Zhaoxin and Xiong Changren, 1991).

Although irradiation is very effective in improving the nutritional value of fibrous crop residues, it remains unfeasible at the farm level.

High pressure steaming

High pressure steaming (also called "Heat spurt" by the inventor) to improve the nutritive value of low quality feeds was closely studied at the Inner Mongolian Academy of Animal Sciences (He Jian *et al.*, 1989). Ground wheat straw or other crop residues are placed in a closed steel tank and saturated with high pressure steam. When the expected temperature (or pressure) and time are reached, a tank valve is suddenly opened allowing materials to enter a pressure-release tank through a specially designed tube. This high pressure steaming and explosion result in a brown straw with looser structure. High pressure steaming markedly decreases straw CF (Table 2-7) and therefore increases the *in vitro* DM digestibility (Table 2-8). Results from an *in situ* study (He Jian *et al.*, 1989) showed that NDF digestibility (48 hour incubation) of the treated wheat straw was increased by 68 percent (38 to 69) in rumen-fistulated sheep and by 233 percent (19 to 62) with caecum-fistulated pigs. Rumen VFA concentration was also increased 9.9 percent (55.3 vs 50.6 mM/litre) in sheep fed diets based on the high pressure steamed wheat straw, compared to untreated straw. In lamb feeding trials (Hou Guizhi *et al.*, 1997), animals were fed equal amounts of mixed concentrate and wheat straw per day per animal (230 g dry weight). Lambs fed high pressure steamed straw ate more of it (433-595 g DM) and gained faster (44.8-50.3 g) than lambs with untreated straw (intake of 413-535 g DM and gains of 18.6-18.8 g).

Compared with chemical treatment, high-pressure steam does not require reagents and thus minimizes potential environmental pollution. In relation to other physical treatments, high-pressure steam is more effective in improving crop residue nutritive value. However, it implies high investment for equipment and a steam generator, and it has not been developed for wider utilization throughout the country.

Table 2-7. Composition (% of DM) of wheat straw after high-pressure steaming

	DM	CP	CF	Ash
Before steaming	91.7	2.57	43.5	4.4
After steaming	94.8	2.84	37.8	9.1

SOURCE: He Jian *et al.*, 1989; Lu Dexun *et al.*, 1990.
KEY: DM = dry matter, CP = crude protein, CF = crude fibre.

Table 2-8. *In vitro* digestibility (%) of fibrous feeds after high-pressure steaming

	WS	CS	RS(1)	RS(2)	SD
Before steaming	38.7	52.1	40.1	40.3	24.9
After steaming	55.5	75.5	59.6	52.7	43.3

SOURCE: He Jian *et al.* (1989).
KEY: WS = wheat straw; CS = corn [maize] stover; RS(1) & RS(2) = rice straw samples; SD = sawdust.

Chemical treatment

Since the beginning of the 19th century, attempts have been made to improve the digestibility and nutritive value of crop residues. A major breakthrough was chemical treatment to remove encrusting substances (cellulose, hemicellulose and lignin). Many chemicals have been screened in laboratory experiments for their potential to enhance digestibility. However, only three are being routinely used in animal research: sodium hydroxide (NaOH), ammonia (NH$_3$), and calcium hydroxide (CaOH).

The modes of action of chemical treatment on crop residues, especially with alkalis, have been described by Klopfenstein (1981):

(1) hemicellulose solubilization,

(2) increases in cellulose and hemicellulose digestion, and

(3) increases in digestion rate for cellulose and hemicellulose.

The data on ammoniation of maize stover and rice straw from many studies (Mao Huaming and Feng Yanglian, 1991; Meng Qingxiang, 1988; Xing Tingxian, 1995; Ji Yilun *et al.*, 1988; Gu Chuipeng *et al.*, 1988a; Liu Jianxin *et al.*, 1992) support these modes of action for the chemical treatment.

Sodium hydroxide treatment

Sodium hydroxide treatment of crop residues has been investigated and used in some areas of the country since the late 1970s. The procedure basically followed the "dry method," where NaOH is applied at 3-5 percent and the moisture content is 20-30 percent of DM. Alkali treatment may saponify the ester bonds between lignin and carbohydrates or the phenolic acid-carbohydrate complexes in plant cell wall. Through these effects, structural carbohydrates in both lignified and unlignified plant tissues become more digestible, with consequent increases in rate and digestibility

The treatment with NaOH results in increases in crop residue palatability and digestibility, and in animal performance (Xiong Yiqiang, 1986). Steers fed rations based on NaOH-treated wheat straw gained 20 percent faster than did the control group when concentrate was half of total ration (Sun Qinghai, 1985). Ye Risong *et al.* (1999) reported that dairy cows fed NaOH-treated rice straw diets ingested 1.9 kg (86.4 percent) more straw and produced 1.4 kg (7.9 percent) more milk per day than those on untreated-straw diets.

Although NaOH treatment works effectively in improving the nutritive value of crop residues, NaOH is expensive, corrosive and its use may result in significant excretion of sodium ions in animal excreta. Long-term accumulation of sodium may lead to soil fertility problems and environmental pollution. Thus, application of NaOH treatment of crop residues is not popular with the farmers at present.

Ammoniation
Since the middle of 1980s, ammoniation of crop residues has drawn a great deal of attention in China due to several advantages: effectiveness in improving digestibility, addition of non-protein nitrogen to treated residues, and absence of sodium accumulation in soils. Ammoniation is dealt with in Chapter 3.

Most data have shown a decreased NDF content, but little change in ADF and ADL contents of crop residues due to ammoniation (Meng Qingxiang, 1988; Wu Keqian, 1996; Xing Tingxian, 1995). The results suggest that ammoniation can break the linkage between hemicellulose and lignin and make the hemicellulose fraction partially soluble to NDF solution. The soluble hemicellulose would be highly digestible by ruminal micro-organisms. After being ammoniated, treated crop residues have an increased N content relative to untreated residues (Table 2-9).

Many *in vitro* and *in vivo* digestion trials have been conducted to evaluate the effect of ammoniation on digestibility of different crop residues. Ten studies with ammoniated crop residues indicated an average increase in digestibility of

Table 2-9. Effect of ammoniation on composition (% of DM) of crop residues

CP		NDF		ADF		ADL		Source
UNT	AMM	UNT	AMM	UNT	AMM	UNT	AMM	
Wheat straw								
3.5	9.1	89.1	78.9	53.7	54.2	14.3	14.1	Meng, 1988
2.8	6.6	78.1	69.2	51.3	51.3	19.7	14.5	Wu, 1996
-	-	84.2	76.4	50.3	49.9	15.1	14.6	Cao *et al.*, 2000
3.3	9.6	-	-	-	-	18.7	17.1	Zhang *et al.*, 1982
4.2	4.5	77.7	75.9	51.3	49.4	10.1	9.9	Xing, 1995
Rice straw								
-	-	69.7	65.9	51.2	47.2	12.0	10.4	Cao *et al.*, 2000
6.1	13.5	75.0	71.4	49.9	48.7	8.7	8.3	Gu *et al.*, 1988a
5.6	10.1	-	-	-	-	11.3	9.8	Zhang *et al.*, 1982
3.7	7.3	67.2	65.0	48.6	45.1	5.1	5.2	Xing, 1995
Maize stover								
6.9	11.0	-	-	-	-	-	-	Zhang *et al.*, 1982
10.7	27.2	69.4	63.9	38.7	36.2	4.7	4.6	Xing, 1995

KEY: UNT = untreated; AMM = ammoniated; CP = crude protein; NDF = neutral detergent fibre; ADF = acid detergent fibre; ADL = acid detergent lignin.

24.3 percent (12.4-44.6) or 11.2 (6.4-17.8) percentage units. Animals ingested ammoniated residues faster than the untreated (Table 2-10).

Improvements in the feeding value of crop residues due to ammoniation have been observed in many feeding trials. Some of the results are summarized in Table 2-11.

Computer simulation results on beef production under different practical conditions were always in favour of ammoniated wheat straw over untreated straw when comparison was made on the basis of maximum benefit per unit of body weight gain (Meng Qingxiang *et al.*, 1990b).

Table 2-10. Effect of ammoniation on ingestion rate of crop residues

Residue	Treatment	Animal	Intake rate[1]	Source
Wheat straw	Ammoniated	Native steer	25.7	Zhang et al, 1982
	Untreated	Native steer	42.1	
	Ammoniated	Crossbred cattle	59.0	Du et al.,1992
	Untreated	Crossbred cattle	94.0	
Rice straw	Ammoniated	Dairy heifer	25.7	Lu et al., 1984
	Untreated	Dairy heifer	44.0	
Maize stover	Ammoniated	Native steer	20.2	Zhang et al., 1982
	Untreated	Native steer	23.5	
	Ammoniated	Crossbred cattle	49.4	Du et al.,1992
	Untreated	Crossbred cattle	68.4	
Soy straw	Ammoniated	Goat	42.0	Chen and Li, 1998
	Untreated	Goat	45.0	

NOTE: (1) Intake rate is expressed as time (minutes) spent in ingestion of one kg of roughage.

Table 2-11. Effect on herbivore growth of ammoniation of crop residues

Residue	Animal species	DM intake (kg/day)		BW gain (g/day)		Gain/Feed (%)	
		UNT	AMM	UNT	AMM	UNT	AMM
Wheat straw	Native steers [1]	4.42	5.17	266	630	6.0	11.0
	Native steers [2]	7.43	7.96	574	722	7.7	9.1
	Native steers [3]	3.68	5.35	270	570	7.3	10.7
	Crossbred bulls [4]	10.29	11.16	860	1120	8.4	10.1
	Lambs [5]	0.50	0.73	-67	19	-13.5	2.6
	Dairy heifers [6]	6.58	7.45	324	613	4.9	7.9
Rice straw	Native steers [1]	5.04	5.99	935	1226	18.6	20.5
	Dairy heifers [7]	6.72	7.72	494	728	7.4	9.4
	Goats [8]	1.71	1.75	85	112	5.0	6.4
Maize stover	Steers [1]	6.03	6.77	607	830	10.1	12.3
	Dairy heifers [1]	8.51	9.38	830	950	9.7	10.1
	Horses [1]	5.07	5.94	116	186	2.3	3.1

SOURCES: (1) Zhang Tianzeng et al., 1982; (2) Wu Keqian, 1996; (3) Meng Qingxiang, 1990a; (4) Cao Yufeng et al., 2000; (5) Yuan Zhizhao et al., 1986; (6) Jiang Zhijie et al., 1986; (7) Lu Donglin et al., 1984; (8) Chen Ruirong and Li Yongfu, 1998.
KEY: BW = body weight; UNT = untreated; AMM = ammoniated.

The maximum benefit is expressed as minimum concentrate consumption per unit gain, or minimum feed cost per unit gain. Based on the beef market situation at that time, a two-stage feeding optimized system was proposed (Meng Qingxiang *et al.*, 1990b). During the first period (from birth to 250 kg)

with minimum concentrate consumption per unit gain, cattle should be fed a largish amount of ammoniated crop residues to maintain a relatively low rate of daily gain (300-500 g). During the finishing period (250 to 450 kg) with minimum feed cost per unit gain, cattle were to be fed on low crop residue and high concentrate diets to allow faster gain rates (> 1 000 g/day). The computer simulation results from this two-stage feeding system compare well to actual feeding results from Beijing, Shandong, Shanxi and Henan (Table 2-12).

In another study, Meng and Xiong (1993) found that lambs fed ammoniated

Table 2-12. Beef cattle growth from computer simulation and actual feeding studies

tem	n[1]	Concentrate level (%)	Daily gain (g)	Concentrate per unit gain (kg/kg)	Feed cost per unit gain (¥/kg)
		Growth period			
Simulation	-	38.8	718	3.59	2.62
Actual feeding	24	40.0	846	3.44	2.71
		Finishing period			
Simulation	-	70.6	1168	4.04	2.55
Actual feeding	40	72.0	1069	4.71	2.61

Source: Meng Qingxiang et al., 1990b. Note: (1) Number of cattle used in the study

wheat straw had increased dietary intake, body weight gain and better concentrate conversion efficiency compared with animals fed untreated wheat straw. The magnitude of the improvement gradually declined with increasing proportion of mixed concentrates in the diet. Regression showed that feeding ammoniated straw diets to lambs could benefit either by increased daily gain at similar concentrate level, or by less concentrate feed consumption at the same rate of gain. Based on the results, it was calculated that each tonne of ammoniated wheat straw replacing untreated straw could produce 105.2 kg (37-159.2 kg) more of liveweight gain at concentrate levels from 22 to 72 percent. When lambs gained at equal rates, each tonne of ammoniated wheat straw could save about 285.4 kg (71.9-593.1 kg) of mixed concentrates or grains at the above range of concentrate levels. This conclusion agrees well with experience from commercial animal production: each tonne of ammoniated crop residues when replacing untreated residues could save 250-300 kg of grain in cattle or sheep (Guo Tingshuang, 1996).

Many studies have also demonstrated that feeding ammoniated crop residues greatly improved lactating performance of dairy cows. Table 2-13 summarizes the results of 4 trials and shows that ammoniation of crop residues increased actual yield on average by 1.7 kg (20.1 vs 18.4 kg) without changes in milk composition, including fat percentage.

Table 2-13. Effect of ammoniation on lactation performance of dairy cows

Residue	Treatment	n[1]	Milk (kg/d)	FCM kg/d	Milk fat (%)	Source
Wheat straw	Ammoniated	6	21.4	21.0	3.78	Song *et al.*, 1998
	Untreated	6	18.4	18.0	3.68	
	Ammoniated	6	22.3	20.6	3.48	Wang *et al.*, 1996
	Untreated	6	22.0	20.1	3.42	
Maize stover	Ammoniated	8	20.1	18.8	3.57	Ma and Zhu, 1997
	Untreated	8	17.5	16.4	3.59	
	Ammoniated	6	16.4	16.3	3.98	Zhang *et al.*, 1995
	Untreated	6	15.7	15.4	3.88	

NOTE: (1) Number of cows in each study.
KEY: FCM = fat-corrected milk yield

Other treatments

Since limestone is available cheaply in China, the use of $Ca(OH)_2$ to treat crop residues attracted a great deal of interest from the 1950s. Calcium hydroxide is generally less effective in treating crop residues than other alkaline sources, such as NaOH or NH_3. Combining $Ca(OH)_2$ with urea or other alkalis seems to solve this problem. Combining $Ca(OH)_2$ with urea, Mao Huaming and Feng Yanglian (1991) showed that rice and wheat straw treatment increased the CP content by 3.5 times (8.3 vs 3.1 percent) and *in situ* DM digestibility by 69.8 percent (65.9 vs 38.8). In a feeding trial (Feng Yanglian, 1996), dairy heifers fed such treated rice straw showed significant increases in dietary DM intake (from 6.56 to 6.89 kg), weight gains (from 829 to 898 g/day), feed conversion (7.9:1 to 7.6:1) as compared with those fed the untreated straw.

Cao Yufeng *et al.* (2000) reported significant improvements in the nutritive value of wheat and rice straws as a result of combination treatment with urea, calcium hydroxide and common salt. Table 2-14 shows the changes in NDF, ADF, ADL, cellulose and hemicellulose content and *in vitro* DM digestibility before and after treatment. Combined treatment reduced the content of NDF, ADF and hemicellulose, but did not change the content of cellulose and lignin over the untreated straw. The *in vitro* DM digestibility of treated straws was enhanced relative to untreated straws. Growth performance data with cross-bred beef cattle fed the combined, ammoniated or untreated rice straw diets are presented in Table 2-15. Cattle fed the combined diets had somewhat more dietary DM intake, better daily gain, improved feed conversion and considerably reduced feed cost per kg of weight gain than cattle on either untreated or ammoniated straw diet.

Table 2-14. Effect of combined treatment on composition (as % of DM) and digestibility (%) of wheat and rice straw

	NDF	ADF	CEL	HC	ADL	IVDMD
		Wheat Straw				
Untreated	84.2	50.3	33.6	33.9	15.1	36.2
Urea + Ca(OH)$_2$ + salt	74.5	47.4	32.5	27.0	14.2	43.7
		Rice straw				
Untreated	69.7	51.2	34.6	18.6	12.0	40.9
Urea + Ca(OH)$_2$ + salt	61.4	45.4	30.5	16.0	9.9	51.2

SOURCE: Cao Yufeng *et al.*, 2000.
KEY: NDF = neutral detergent fibre; ADF = acid detergent fibre; CEL = cellulose;
HC = hemicellulose; IVDMD = *in vitro* dry matter digestibility.

Table 2-15. Effect of combined treatment of rice straw on growth of cross-bred beef cattle

Treatment	DM intake (kg/d)	Average daily gain (kg)	Feed/Gain ratio	Cost/Gain (¥/kg)
Untreated	9.1	0.86	12.0	5.85
Ammoniated	9.9	1.12	10.0	4.81
Urea + Ca(OH)$_2$+ salt	10.3	1.28	9.0	4.17

SOURCE: Cao Yufeng *et al.*, 2000.

Other combination methods for treatment of crop residues with sodium hydroxide and urea (Shi Chuanlin, 1998), ammoniation and enzyme (Chen Sanyou *et al.*, 1998), and ammoniation and ensilage (Wang Xiaochun *et al.*, 1996) have also been reported elsewhere. In each case, the nutritive value was improved, but these methods have not so far been taken into practice.

Biological approach

Regular ensilage
This popular method is described in Chapter 4.

Microbial ensilage

Ensilage of whole fresh maize plants is only practised for large-scale feedlots and dairy farms. For small-scale family farms, ensiling dry crop residues after reconstitution of moisture is usually the best way for preserving feeds, since farmers do not have suitable equipment to quickly harvest their cereal plants. Another reason is that they have to sow promptly the next crop in most regions with a double-cropping system. Ensiling dry crop residues involves actions such as chopping, reconstitution of moisture, pressing and mixing with certain additives, including micro-organisms such as lactic acid producing bacteria, cellulolytic bacteria, for proper fermentation and nutrient preservation.

A large number of dry crop residues have been successfully ensiled with addition of microbial products in China in recent years. This method is commonly called "microbial ensilage," or *Weizhu* in Chinese. Some bacterial products with specialized functions and warranted quality have been developed and approved for practical use by the government. Wu Keqian (1996) and Meng Qingxiang *et al.* (1999) ensiled wheat straw with addition of a specific microbial product containing bacteria that function as lactic acid and propionic acid producers and cellulose degraders, and fed it to cross-bred steers. The results showed that microbial ensiling resulted in reduction of NDF, ADF, cellulose and hemicellulose, and an increase in *in situ* DM digestibility (Table 2-16). In some feeding studies, it was shown that microbial ensilage of crop residues such as wheat straw, rice straw, maize stover or soybean straw caused increased daily gains, feed intake and feed conversion, and decreased feed cost per unit gain in growing ruminants (Table 2-17). Several studies (Zhang Yang and Meng Dongli, 1995; Chen Xiling *et al.*, 1995; Ma Yusheng and Zhu Guosheng, 1997) also indicated that lactating cows fed diets based on microbial ensiled straw had increased milk and fat-corrected yield, and slightly higher milk fat percentages, compared with diets based on untreated straw.

Table 2-16. Composition of wheat straw before and after microbial ensiling

	DM	Composition (% of DM)					ISDMD	Source
	(%)	NDF	ADF	CEL	HC	ADL	(%)	
Untreated	87	78	51	32	27	20	42	Wu, 1996
Microbial	33	70	50	33	20	16	46	
Untreated	-	83	60	45	23	15	37	Meng *et al.*, 1999
Microbial	-	79	57	43	21	14	41	

KEY: NDF = neutral detergent fibre; ADF = acid detergent fibre; CEL = cellulose; HC = hemi-cellulose; ISDMD = *in situ* dry matter digestibility.

Table 2-17. Effect of microbial ensilage of crop residues on animal growth

Residue Species	Concentrate (g/day)	Treatment	ADG (g)	Intake (kg DM)	Feed/Gain	Cost (¥/kg)
Soybean straw	150	Untreated	0.09	1.72	20.2	
(goats) [1]	150	Microbial	0.12	1.88	15.9	
Wheat straw	1 800	Untreated	0.62	5.88	9.4	6.40
(steers) [2]	1 800	Microbial	0.77	6.50	8.5	5.51
Wheat straw	3 300	Untreated	0.57	7.43	12.9	8.33
(steers) [3]	3 300	Microbial	0.89	8.22	9.2	5.66

SOURCES:(1) Chen Ruirong and Li Yongfu, 1998; (2) Meng Qingxiang *et al.*, 1999;
(3) Wu Keqian, 1996.
KEY: ADG = average daily gain.

Another significant effect of microbial ensilage of dry crop residues is probably to hydrate and weaken plant structures so that less energy is expended on rumination. Ensiled crop residues usually have good palatability for ruminants, and thus high intake. In comparison with ammoniated straw, microbial ensiled residues give higher intake, faster rate of passage and therefore better performance. Other advantage of microbial ensilage is its low input cost for acquiring microbial products and accessories, e.g. plastic sheets, and therefore microbial ensilage is considered a better method to enhance the feeding value of dry crop residues. However, microbial ensilage generally results in lower digestibility than ammoniation (Wu Keqian, 1996). Another disadvantage of microbial ensilage includes substantial loss (usually 5-10 percent of DM) of organic material that would otherwise be rapidly fermented in the rumen. As a result, it is still argued academically whether the anaerobic ensilage of such ready digestible materials within crop residues is economically beneficial to the animal. Further in-depth research is required to select bacteria strains that selectively degrade cell wall fractions, especially lignocelluloses.

Treatment with White Rot fungi
Because White Rot fungi can effectively attack lignin and cellulose, their use to treat lignocellulosic material to increase digestibility has been studied quite extensively in other countries, but little in China. Xiao Xunjun (1998) and Peng Jun (1998) at China Agricultural University treated wheat straw with strains of *Cyathus stercoreus, Bjerkandera adusta, Dichomitus squalens, Pleurotus* spp. and *Pleurotus ostreatus* for 30 days, and showed that treatment decreased NDF from 71.4 (control) to 67.4, 59.2, 62.7, 65.0 and 67.9 percent, and ADF from

53.1 to 50.3, 45.1, 46.0, 50.0 and 51.3 percent, respectively. After fermentation by the five fungus strains, a considerable loss was found in lignin, from 23 to 44 percent, and in DM, from 11 to 17 percent. There was no apparent loss in cellulose and hemicellulose (Xiao Xunjun, 1998). When wheat straw was incubated *in vitro* with mixed rumen micro-organisms for 24 hours, DM digestibility was increased 11 and 8 percent for the treatment with *Bjerkandera adusta* and *Phleurtus* spp., respectively, compared with the untreated control. Straw digestibility with the other three strains did not change. When activity of polysaccharide-degrading enzymes (FPase, avicelase, CMCase, xylanase) and ligninase (Mn-dependent peroxidase) was measured, Peng Jun (1998) found that enzyme activity varied considerably with different fungus strains. It was also noted that most White Rot fungi grew slowly on common crop residues and could not effectively compete against other microbes. These observations suggest that effective breakdown of crop residue cell walls by White Rot fungi in practice will require selection or creation of better strains, and also further refinement of the current treatment techniques.

Use of mushroom-substrate residues

Crop residues have been used as a substrate to grow mushrooms. This practice is a very profitable business in some areas of the country. The substrate residue after mushroom harvest can be used to feed animals. The most commonly used crop residues are cottonseed hulls, wheat straw, rice straw and maize stover. The residues usually have higher CP and lower CF contents compared with the original substrate. Yang Xunyi *et al.* (1986) reported that after the 2nd, 3rd and 4th harvest of mushrooms, the CP content of the residual substrate increased by 32.5, 44.2 and 60.9 percent, while its CF content reduced by 42.4, 48.1 and 50.4 percent, respectively. When the substrate residue was included in growing pig diets at level of 5 percent (replacing half of the wheat bran), there was no significant difference in average daily gain and feed conversion (Liu Jianchang *et al.*, 1998). However, growth performance of pigs decreased with increased substrate residue inclusion (Zhou Zongwang, 1991). The only benefit from inclusion of the substrate residues at a low rate in pig diet is the decreased consumption of concentrate or feed cost per unit of body weight gain (Lu Zuozhou *et al.*, 1995b).

Undoubtedly, the use of crop residues for mushroom production is a very good approach in China's agro-ecosystem. Research data have also indicated that some species or strains of mushrooms have strong enzymatic activities digesting cellulose and lignin. Regarding the feeding value of this residue, however, more work remains to be done before any overall recommendations can be given.

Enzymatic treatment

The use of enzymes to attack the lignocellulose structure of crop residues for enhancing their feeding value has been attractive. Crude enzyme products, with cellulolytic and hemicellulolytic capability, are usually added to fibrous feeds in attempts to improve their digestibility. Wang An (1998) observed that treatment of maize stover with an enzyme product, prepared from *Trichoderma viride*, reduced the contents of some cell wall components and enhanced the ruminal digestibility in sheep (Table 2-18). Huang Jianhua (1998) and Huang Jianhua *et al.* (1998) treated maize stover and spent grain from malting (60:40) with an enzyme mixture containing cellulase, proteinase and amylase, and measured the effects on the performance of finishing pigs and laying hens. Inclusion of 10 percent of the treated maize stover and spent grain mixture in the diet did not affect gain rate of pigs or egg production of hens, but reduced by ¥ 0.25 the feed cost per kg of liveweight gain with the pigs (Huang Jianhua, 1998) and by ¥ 0.49 per kg of egg production with the laying hens (Huang Jianhua *et al.*, 1998).

Table 2-18. Effect of cellulase addition to maize stover on fibre fraction content and *in situ* digestibility in sheep

Item	Control	With cellulase
	Chemical composition (%)	
NDF	58.2	56.2
ADF	37.3	35.3
ADL	4.9	4.5
CEL	32.3	29.8
HEM	20.9	20.9
	Digestibility (%)	
DM	39.8	45.8
NDF	27.4	31.3
ADF	29.4	31.7
ADL	16.0	17.8
CEL	31.5	33.7
HEM	23.6	30.5

SOURCE: Wang An, 1998.

KEY: NDF = neutral detergent fibre; ADF = acid detergent fibre; ADL = acid detergent lignin; CEL = cellulose; HEM = hemicellulose; DM = dry matter.

Commercial cellulase products were also added to diets to increase the supply of readily available carbohydrate. When the enzyme products were included at 0.1-0.2 percent of the diet of pigs, cattle and geese, animal performance was considerably improved (Table 2-19). Chen Xiafu *et al.* (1986) also reported the use of crude enzyme products prepared from *Trichoderma viride* as feed additives for growing rabbits. In eight growth trials, rabbits fed on a diet with addition of the cellulolytic enzymes gained 17.5-39.3 percent faster than the control. The difference was consistent and highly significant (< 0.05).

Table 2-19. Effects of cellulase addition on animal performance

Animal	Enzyme level (%)	Item		Treatment		Source
				Control	Enzyme	
Growing pig	0.1	Dietary DMI	(g)	935	1010	Wang, 1998
	0.1	Daily gain	(g)	325	348	Wang, 1998
	0.1	Feed/Gain		2.88	2.90	Wang, 1998
Beef cattle	0.1	Daily gain	(g)	794	942	Chen *et al.*, 1998
Dairy cow	0.1	Grain DMI	(kg)	8.71	9.52	Lu and Wang, 1990
	0.1	Milk yield	(kg)	17.0	17.6	Lu and Wang, 1990
	0.1	Milk yield	(kg)	19.2	21.1	Wang, 1998
	0.2	Milk yield	(kg/day)	26.4	28.6	Su *et al.*, 1997
	0.2	Milk fat	(%)	3.43	3.41	Su *et al.*, 1997
Goose	0.2	Gain	(g)	25.8	41.3	Zhao, 1999

KEY: DMI = dry matter intake.

Although there is a tendency toward increased use of cellulolytic enzymes in animal feeds, at present the cost of suitable enzymes is too high for commercial use. Obviously, advances in biotechnology and increased production of effective enzymes would be expected to lower the cost of enzymatic treatment.

Chapter 3

Ammoniation of crop residues

Zhang Zhishan
Ministry of Agriculture
Yan Qiaojuan
China Agricultural University

INTRODUCTION

As early as 1933, a German scientist started research on straw treatment with ammonia. In 1938, scientists in the former Soviet Union treated wheat straw with anhydrous ammonia to increase digestibility. In the 1950s, a Danish patent was issued on ammonia treatment technology. From the 1970s, Bangladesh, Canada, Denmark, Egypt, India, Japan, Niger, Norway, Tunisia, United Kingdom and USA started research on straw ammoniation. Some countries have popularized ammoniation at national level. Straw ammoniation technologies were introduced to Norway in 1975 with government financial support, and in 1988 total straw treatment had reached 130 thousand tonne, 17.3 percent of total straw output. For environmental protection, Denmark recently prohibited straw burning.

Chinese farmers have known that human urine can be used to treat straw for cattle feed. It is pity that no research has been done on this. From the 1980s, China started to adjust its animal production structure with a new policy of a grain saving strategy. Fundamental research and experiments were started. MOA began to popularize straw ammoniation in 1987. In 1989, straw ammoniation became one of ten key extension techniques of MOA, and by 1993 it had been popularized throughout the country, with 11.7 million tonne of straw treated, the largest in the world. FAO and UNDP had several successful projects on straw utilization for feeding animals. At FAO's suggestion, international conferences on *Increasing Animal Production with Local Resources* were organized in China on three occasions. These conferences provided the opportunity to exchange experiences among different countries.

THE PRINCIPLE AND EFFECTS OF STRAW AMMONIATION

The main component of straw is fibre, including cellulose and hemicellulose that can be digested by ruminants. Some cellulose and hemicellulose are bound to lignin and resistant to microbial attack. The role of ammoniation is to destroy this link, so these fractions are available to the animal. Ammoniation usually increases digestibility by 20 percent and CP content up to 1-2 times. It can also improve palatability and consumption rate. The total nutritional value can be doubled, reaching 0.4-0.5 feed units for each kilogram of ammoniated straw. In addition, ammoniation reduces mould development, destroys weed seeds (e.g. wild oat, false sorghum, etc.), parasite eggs and bacteria.

AMMONIA SOURCES FOR STRAW AMMONIATION

The sources of ammonia to treat straw include anhydrous ammonia, urea, ammonium bicarbonate and aqueous ammonia.

Anhydrous ammonia
Anhydrous ammonia means "ammonia without water." Its formula is NH_3, and its N content is 28.3 percent. The normal dosage is 3 percent by weight of the straw DM. It is the most economical source of ammonia.

The boiling point of anhydrous ammonia is -33.3°C, its vapour density is 0.59 (that of air is 1) and its liquid density 0.62 (that of water is 1). Gas pressure is 1.1 kg/cm^2 at -17.8°C and 13.9 kg/cm^2 38°C. At normal temperature and pressure, anhydrous ammonia is a gas. Expensive pressure containers are required not only to keep it as a liquid, but also to transport and store it. Anhydrous ammonia is a potentially dangerous and toxic material, and stringent safety precautions need to be observed when using it. Its natural ignition temperature is 651°C. If the ammonia content in the air reaches 20 percent, an explosion from self-ignition could occur. Attention should be paid to possible ammonia explosions, even though it seldom happens.

Urea

The N content of urea is 46.7 percent. Its formula is $CO(NH_2)_2$. It is decomposed into ammonia and CO_2 by ureases at ambient temperature. The chemical reaction is:

$$CO(NH_2)_2 + H_2O \xrightarrow{\text{Urease enzymes. Ambient temperature}} 2NH_3\uparrow + CO_2$$

Urea dosage needed to treat straw may vary a lot. The recommended dosage is 4-5 percent urea on DM basis, taking into consideration the effect of ammoniation and costs. Urea can be transported conveniently at normal temperature and pressure. It is harmless to humans. Treating straw with urea does not need complex equipment and the sealing conditions are not as strict as with anhydrous ammonia. It is known that farmers in Bangladesh ammoniate straw in bamboo baskets lined and covered with leaves of a kind of banana. From the *Yellow Cattle Magazine*, it is known that, in Anhui province, technicians use urea as a source of ammonia to treat straw without cover and get good results, which is beneficial for extension of straw ammoniation to rural areas. At present, urea is a widely used source of ammonia in China. Urea is not as effective as anhydrous ammonia for straw treatment, but it is better than ammonium bicarbonate.

Ammonium bicarbonate

The nitrogen content of ammonium bicarbonate is 15-17 percent; its formula is NH_4HCO_3. It can be decomposed into NH_3, CO_2 and H_2O at a suitable temperature (above 60°C). The chemical reaction is:

$$NH_4HCO_3 \xrightarrow{\text{Heating}} NH_3\uparrow + CO_2 + H_2O$$

The dosage of ammonium bicarbonate, estimated by its N content, is 14-19 percent of straw DM. But, according to the experiments carried out in Zhejiang and Shanxi Agricultural Universities, using 8-12 percent of ammonium bicarbonate can give the same result as with 14-19 percent.

Ammonium bicarbonate is a major product of the fertilizer industry and it is readily available at low price. It has a retail price of ¥ 300/ton (compared to more than ¥ 1000 for urea) and it is easy to use. Since ammonium bicarbonate is an intermediate product of urea breakdown, theoretically, in the right concentration, its effect should be similar to urea. Reports from Zhejiang Agricultural University indicate that in the humid south, straw ammoniated with urea showed more mould spots than with ammonium bicarbonate. It does not decompose completely at low temperature, thus in cold climates the effectiveness of treatment with ammonium bicarbonate is not good. When treating with ammonium bicarbonate in an oven, one day is enough, since the temperature reaches 90 °C and it decomposes completely.

Aqueous ammonia
Aqueous ammonia is a solution of ammonia in water. The concentration is quite variable, but the usual value is 20 percent. At this concentration, the normal dosage is 12 percent by weight of straw DM. It is only adapted to areas near to fertilizer factories because its low N content makes transport expensive.

Other sources
Besides the above sources of ammonia, human and animal urine also can be used to treat straw. However, collection difficulties limit practical applications.

METHODS FOR AMMONIA TREATMENT OF STRAW

At present, the methods for popular ammonia treatment of straw in China include stack, silo or bunker, and oven methods. Each uses a different ammonia source.

Stack method
The procedure for the stack method is as follows. First, an area is selected with an elevated, dry and even surface. This area is covered with non-toxic polyethylene sheet and the baled or loose straw (chopped or whole) is stacked on it. It is better to bale straw or to chop it into pieces. Especially for hard and thick maize stover, chopping before treatment facilitates feeding, saves plastic and reduces the danger of puncturing the plastic. The moisture content of straw should be adjusted to 20 percent or more during stacking (anhydrous ammonia requires a low-moisture straw compared with urea and ammonium bicarbonate). The high moisture has a positive effect on straw treatment. However, after

treatment, it is difficult to ventilate the straw and it can be easily attacked by mould. A wooden bar, which will be pulled out when ammonia injection starts, is placed before stacking so that ammonia can be injected easily and conveniently. The stack is sealed with non-toxic polyethylene sheet and injected with 3 percent anhydrous ammonia by weight of straw DM. At the end, the hole left when the pipe is removed is sealed with good quality tape.

Operators working with ammonia must be trained and should strictly follow relevant regulations to ensure personal safety. Treatment time varies inversely with temperature. For example, more than four weeks are needed at a temperature of 5-15°C, but only one week at >30°C.

Straw treatment with anhydrous ammonia is simple and efficient, but particularly suited for large-scale use. The method also had been widely applied in developed countries. It requires some expensive equipment. For instance, the cost of an EQ144 ammonia truck tank carrying 5.1 tonne is ¥ 16 000; a 200-kg ammonia bottle costs ¥ 2 500; a 400-kg bottle costs ¥ 4 500; and an 8.82 kW four-wheel tractor costs ¥ 8 000. Furthermore, anhydrous ammonia is not well suited for private farmers because of its dangers.

In order to explore the best supply system of ammonia for farmers, ammoniation stations have been built in Hebei Xingtai region, Boxiang county; Baoding region, Dingxing county; and Henan Zhoukou region, Fugou county. These stations have accumulated experiences during the past few years to share with other regions.

Selection of plastic film

The basic requirements for plastic film are that it is non-toxic, durable and suitable for sealing. The plastic often used is polyethylene. Thickness, width and colour are determined by practical situations. Thick film (about 0.12 mm) is used for maize stover; thin film (less than 0.12 mm) for wheat straw. Width of film is determined by the size of stack and market availability. If used in the open air, black colour should be preferred, because it is durable and absorbs solar energy, which heats the stack and shortens treatment time. If used indoors, film colour has no obvious influence on treatment. The amount of film required can be calculated by the size of stack.

Size of bottom sheet: Length = Length of stack + (0.5-0.7) m (overlap)

Width = Width of stack + (0.5-0.7) m

Size of covering sheet: Length = Length of stack + height x 2 + (0.5-0.7) m

Width = Width of stack + height x 2 + (0.5-0.7) m

The ammoniation station in Fugou County made a covering sheet that was especially suitable for a 500-kg wheat straw stack. Covering the stack greatly improves treatment efficiency.

Measurement of the stack density

Weighing the stack is a basic task for straw treatment. It is well known that it is important to inject the correct amount of ammonia: too little ammonia is ineffective; too much ammonia increases the cost and has no further effect on treatment. The exact weight of straw must be known so that the correct amount of ammonia can be applied. But weighing is difficult under field conditions. A simple method is to first measure the average density of stack for various straws, then to multiply it by its volume. Stack density depends upon plant species, moisture content and particle size. Of course, density also varies with time. In order to get reliable data, it is necessary to measure many stacks (at least 8 for each straw type). Density is expressed in kg/m^3. In old stacks, volume is measured first, then it is weighed. New stacks are weighed before stacking and volume measured after. It is very easy to calculate the volume of rectangular and cylinder stacks. The volume of stack with irregular shape may only be estimated. In 1989, 9 stacks of air-dried straw were measured in Boxiang county during the FAO project. The average density was 55 and 79 kg/m^3 for new and old wheat straw, and 79 and 99 kg/m^3 for new and old maize stover, both whole, respectively.

Ammonia dosage measurement

The precision of ammonia injection depends on not only the correct weight of straw but also the correct amount of ammonia. Currently there are two main methods for ammonia injection used in China. One is to inject ammonia into the stack directly from an ammonia truck tank filled in the factory (Figure 3-1), the other is to inject it from a bottle (Figure 3-2).

be designed according to practical needs (number of ammoniations per year, numbers of animals).

There are many types of bunkers. They can be built on the surface, underground, or half-and-half. It is recommended to build rectangular bunkers that, by adding internal walls, can be divided into double or twin bunkers for sequential treatment (Figure 3-3). If a double bunker is used for silage, a second fermentation can be started in the second compartment while straw is being used from the other half. Double bunkers are very common in Henan Zhoukou region. For instance, a bunker with a volume of 2 m³ requires 500 bricks, a bag of cement and a wagon of sand. Its total cost is ¥ 100. The cost of a double-bunker holding 4 m³ is ¥ 200, affordable to farmers. One bunker of 2 m³ can hold 300 kg of wheat straw. The two bunkers can be used in turns. One bunker of ammoniated straw is enough for two cattle for a month. If a bunker is used for silage, one bunker can hold more than 1 000 kg. The silo or bunker method has been well received by farmers.

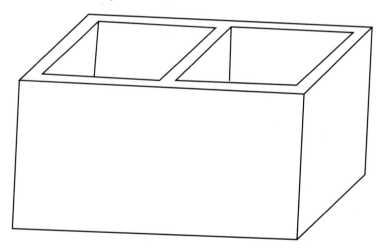

Figure 3-3. A twin bunker

Operation

First, straw is chopped to about 2 cm long. The general principle is that thick and hard residues, such as maize stover, should be cut shorter, while soft materials may be a little bit longer. Then urea (or ammonium bicarbonate) is added to water and stirred to completely dissolve it. Normally, 100 kg of dried straw needs 5 kg urea and 40-60 kg water. Next, the urea solution is sprayed repeatedly over the straw. Before loading the silo, straw can be spread in an open area to facilitate uniformity in spray application. While straw is added to the silo, each layer should be compacted till the bunker is full, and then it is covered with plastic film, held firmly in place by a layer of fine soil (Figure 3-4). Treatment time with urea is a little longer than with anhydrous ammonia.

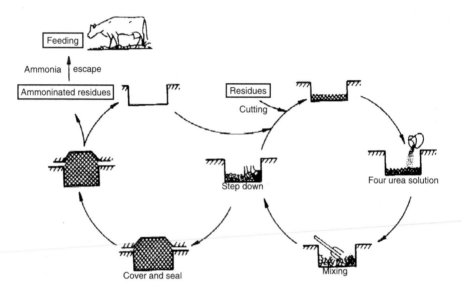

Figure 3-4. Flow chart of the ammoniation of crop residues with urea

When treating straw with urea, the speed of urea decomposition into ammonia should be taken into consideration. It depends on ambient temperature and amount of ureases present in the straw. Decomposition rate increases with temperature, so this method is well adapted to warm regions (or warm seasons). In general, it is suggested to add some substance rich in ureases, such as soybean cake powder, to accelerate urea breakdown. Maize stover contains much more ureases than other cereal straws, so ureases are not required. In China, maize stover is one of the three main crop residues, along with rice and wheat straw. The nutritive value of maize stover is higher than other straws, either before or after ammoniation. However, it was seldom used as feed because it is thick and hard, and not easy to be store and transport. Nowadays it should be preferentially used as feed because processing and treatment methods (chopping, kneading, heat-extrusion, baling and ammonia treatment) are available to overcome these problems.

Oven method

Straw can be quickly treated quickly with ammonia in an oven. The Non-conventional Feed Institute of China Agricultural University has developed a metal, self-assembly oven for ammonia treatment. The oven is composed of a chamber, a heating system, an air circulating system and a straw trailer. The chamber must be insulated, sealed and resistant to corrosion by acid or alkali. The heating device may be an electric heater or a coal-fired steam heater, depending on local conditions. Shanxi Wanrong County used steam to heat the oven, with good results. The straw trailer should be convenient for loading, unloading, transport and heating. A metal mesh trailer with steel wheels is the preferred option.

Operation

Ammonium bicarbonate (8-12 percent of straw DM) is first dissolved in water. Straw (baled or loose; chopped or whole) is placed on the trailer. The solution is uniformly sprayed over the straw, adjusting moisture content to about 45 percent. Once the trailer is full, it is moved into the chamber, the door is closed and heating started. If heating is by electricity, the heating tube needs to be set to control the chamber's temperature at about 95 °C. After heating for 14-15 hours, it is turned off. The chamber should remain sealed for 5-6 hours more, and then the straw trailer is moved outside for ventilation. Once ammonia residues are gone, the straw can be fed.

The oven can shorten treatment time considerably since it only takes 24 hours to treat straw. In addition, oven treatment is not weather dependent, so ammoniation can be done all year round. However, the cost is relatively high, limiting its application. In recent years in Jilin Province, straw has been treated in a coal-heated chamber usually used for flue-curing tobacco. The investment for the oven was avoided and fuel expenses reduced, so treatment cost was greatly decreased.

Other options

Besides the above three widely used methods, there are still some other methods for straw treatment. For instance, ammoniation within plastic bags was readily accepted by farmers due to low initial cost. However, repeated purchases of plastic bags increased costs and restricted wider application. In some places, straw is treated in locally available containers (such as vats). This latter method may be worth advocating.

FACTORS INFLUENCING EFFECTIVENESS OF AMMONIATION

There are a number of factors that influence the effectiveness of straw ammoniation, including dosage, moisture content, temperature and treatment time.

Ammonia dosage

Experiments relating ammonia dosage to digestibility were conducted by Sundstol *et al.* (1978). Results showed a significant improvement in *in vitro* digestibility by increasing ammonia dosage from 1 to 2.5 percent of straw DM, and a slight improvement from 2.5 to 4 percent. There were no further effects beyond 4 percent. In recent years, many similar experiments have been carried out with similar results. The economic optimum ammonia dosage probably lies between 2.5 and 3.5 percent of DM.

When treating straw with anhydrous ammonia, urea, ammonia bicarbonate or aqueous ammonia, the dosage should be estimated by their nitrogen content: 82.3, 46.7, 15 and 20 percent, respectively. As the conversion ratio of nitrogen to ammonia is 1.21, the dosage of other sources can be calculated by the following equation:

$$\text{Dosage (kg)} = \frac{\text{economic optimum for dosage of ammonia}}{\text{nitrogen content of ammonia source} \times 1.21}$$

Optimum dosages (per 100 kg of straw) are: 2.5-3.5 kg for anhydrous ammonia; 4.5-6.2 kg for urea; 13.8-19.3 kg (8-12 kg in practice) for ammonium bicarbonate; and 10.3-14.5 kg for aqueous ammonia (20% N).

Normally, treating 100 kg air-dry straw requires either 3 kg of anhydrous ammonia, 4-5 kg of urea, 8-12 kg of ammonium bicarbonate or 11-12 kg of aqueous ammonia (20% N).

Moisture content of straw

Moisture content of straw is another important factor determining the effectiveness of treatment. Ammonia combines with water to form ammonium hydroxide (NH_4)OH.

Regarding the optimum moisture content of straw, experts from China and abroad have different opinions. Sundstol *et al.* (1979) found that increasing moisture content of straw from 12 to 50 percent had a positive effect on *in vitro* organic matter digestibility (IVOMD) (Figure 3-5), regardless of temperature. With extremely low moisture (3.3 percent), ammonia treatment had no positive effect on enzyme solubility and straw IVOMD. Sundstol and Ekeern (1982) found that a 6-week treatment with 2 percent anhydrous ammonia of straw with 2.5, 5.0, 7.5 and 10.0 percent moisture, produced corresponding IVOMDs of 52.1, 58.5, 59.1 and 66.0 percent, respectively. Treating straw with 15-20 percent moisture with aqueous ammonia (25 percent) was better than with anhydrous ammonia. Aqueous ammonia improved the moisture content of straw. For example, using 2 percent aqueous ammonia to treat straw is equivalent to adding 6 percent water to straw. Experiments proved that the straw IVOMD could be gradually improved by increasing moisture from 2.5 to 50 percent.

Experiments conducted by Professor Ji Yilun of Shanxi Agricultural University indicated that the optimal moisture content of straw was about 45 percent when treated with urea or ammonia bicarbonate. High moisture contents would result in handling problems and greater risk of damage during storage (e.g. mould development).

The positive effect of higher moisture has also been found in practice. Straw from both the top and the bottom of the stack has high digestibility and good intake due to its moisture content. Straw treated by the Animal Bureau of Zhoukou Region in Henan Province during the FAO project in 1989, with the proportions 100 kg straw: 100 kg water: 5kg urea, gave good results despite the high moisture content.

On the whole, higher moisture content of straw may improve digestibility. Moisture content can reach 50 percent or more, if straw can be transported and stored without becoming mouldy.

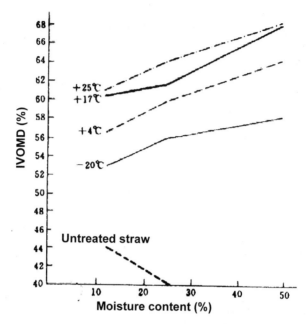

Figure 3-5. Effects of varying moisture contents and treatment temperatures on straw IVOMD when treated with 3.4% ammonia in DM for 8 weeks

Temperature and treatment time

High temperature reduces treatment time, since, in general, chemical reactions occur faster. High temperature had a positive effect on both N content and IVOMD of ammonia-treated straw. At a temperature around 45°C, treatment for 3-7 days greatly improved digestibility, whereas the reaction was extremely slow near -20°C. The season effect on ammonia treatment of oat straw in stacks had been studied by Alibes *et al.* (1983) in Spain, who divided 6 tonne into two parts for treatment in summer (38°C) and in winter (7°C). The results indicated that the CP content, DM digestibility, OM digestibility as well as straw intake were higher for summer treatment by 83, 12, 12.3 and 19.3 percent, respectively. Sundstol *et al.* (1978) treated oat straw containing 12.5 percent moisture and 3.4 percent CP with 3.4 percent NH_3 in DM at temperatures of -20°C, 4°C, 17°C and 24°C for 8 weeks. The CP contents after treatment were 6.5, 7.3, 8.3 and 8.5 percent, respectively. Sundstol *et al.* (1978) believed that ammonia treatment may significantly increased N content at temperatures over 25°C, but in longer treatment times (e.g. 3 weeks) increasing temperature from 40°C to 120°C had no positive effect on IVOMD. The length of treatment time for different temperatures had been given by Sundstol *et al.* (1978):

Temperature (°C)	Treatment time
< 5	> 8 weeks
5-15	4-8 weeks
15-30	1-4 weeks
>30	< 1 week
>90	< 1 day

A closed stack may be stored for a long time without becoming mouldy, and stacks should not be opened before it is necessary to use the treated feed. After opening a stack of ammonia-treated straw, it should be aerated for a time before feeding. In cold climates, increasing treatment time has positive effects on ammoniation, but CP content decreases slowly after opening. Beijing Dairy Institute treated rice straw with 3 percent hydrous ammonia and the CP content of treated straw reached 7.8 percent, but 3 months later was below 7 percent.

Quality of material being treated
In general, straw quality after ammoniation depends a lot on pre-treatment quality. Greater improvement is obtained from low quality materials.

Pressure
High pressure is beneficial for ammonia treatment. Experiments conducted by Lie (1975) indicated that increasing the pressure from 1 to 5 kg/cm^2 had a positive effect on IVOMD. Sundstol and Owen (1984) had carried out experiments with similar results. It is known that if ammoniated straw is wafered or pressed into pellets, N-content and IVOMD can be further improved.

QUALITY EVALUATION OF AMMONIATED STRAW

There are three methods to evaluate quality of ammoniated straw: sensory evaluation, chemical analysis and biological tests. The physical changes in straw can be visually observed as an easy, but imprecise, way to evaluate treated straw quality. By chemical analysis, the components of straw such as CF and CP can be measured, but by itself it can not give an estimate of overall nutritive value and animal intake. The scientific method of evaluation of straw quality is through biological tests. For example, digestibility *in sacco* (in the rumen), cellulase digestibility test, and especially digestibility *in vivo*, can estimate not only the digestibility but also the speed of digestion.

Sensory evaluation

Properly ammoniated straw is soft, brownish yellow or light brown, and with a light fragrance after excess ammonia has evaporated. If straw appears white or grey and is sticky or clumps, it means that it has been attacked by mould. This damaged straw should not be used as feed. Of course, this situation seldom occurs if treatment is correct. Mould normally results from high moisture content, defective sealing or delayed ventilation after opening. If, after ammoniation, straw colour is nearly the same as before treatment, it means that ammoniation did not go very well, but it can still be used as feed.

Chemical analysis

Chemical analysis is being widely used in China at present. This method evaluates the extent of straw quality improvement by analysing the main parameters (as digestibility of DM and CP) before and after ammoniation. Lu Xilei (1991), from the Beijing Dairy Institute, ammoniated straw by ensiling with anhydrous ammonia at 3 percent DM on the farm. Comparisons of the main parameters between ammoniated straw and Chinese wild-rye hay are shown in Table 3-1. After treatment CP content improved by 5.44, 3.98 and 5.02 percent for wheat straw, rice straw and maize stover, respectively. The corresponding figures for digestibility were 10.3, 24.0 and 20.0 percent, respectively. Digestibilities of ammoniated wheat straw and maize stover were nearly the same or higher than Chinese wild-rye hay.

Table 3-1. Nutritional comparison between ammoniated straw and Chinese wild-rye hay

Feed	Nutritive factor (%)			
	DM	CP	CF	DM digestibility
Chinese wild-rye hay	90	5.9	32.0	52.0
Winter wheat straw	90	2.2	41.0	39.7
Ammoniated winter wheat straw	70	7.6	39.0	50.0
Rice straw	93	3.9	33.1	24.0
Ammoniated rice straw	90	7.8	32.5	48.0
Maize stover	90	3.7	30.5	42.0
Ammoniated maize stover	90	8.7	30.5	60.0

SOURCE: Lu Xilei, 1991.

Biological tests

Biological tests, especially the nylon bag *in sacco* method for digestion rate, has been widely applied not only in science and research institutes but also in some production units. For example, in Henan Zhoukou region, the straw degradation rate was measured by the nylon bag technique in sheep during the FAO project (1989-1990). The results, presented in Table 3-2 and Figure 3-6, showed that the maximum rate of degradation (P-value) for ammoniated barley reached 77.1 from 52.1 percent in untreated straw. In the last five years, the Institute of Animal Production and Health in Hebei Province has measured digestibility rates for 9 feedstuffs (89 samples) by the nylon bag technique in sheep. These feeds include beans, cakes, pomace, dregs, animal by-products, leaf and straw. The nylon bag technique provides a foundation for systematic development of the feed resource.

Table 3-2. Nylon bag (*in sacco*) dry matter degradation of wheat straw (%)

Sample	Incubation time (hours)						a	b	c	RSD[1]
	0	8	24	48	72	96				
Ammoniated	16.4	23.7	40.0	55.6	64.8	70.1	13.1	64.4	0.04	1.70
Untreated	12.2	17.0	32.7	44.1	48.1	50.8	4.9	47.3	0.02	0.99

Note: (1) RSD = residual standard deviation

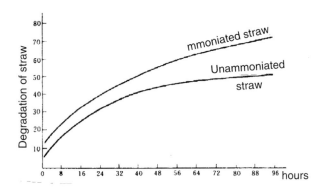

Figure 3-6. Digestibility curve

Straw degradation rate can be calctflated by the equation:

$$p = a+b\ (1-e^{-ct})$$

where:

> p = the amount degraded at time (t)
> a = soluble material which is immediately digestible,
> b = the fraction which will be digested in the given time,
> c = the rate constant for digestion of b,
> $a + b$ = the asymptote or the potential extent of digestion,
> e = natural log
> t = degradation time

The above parameters give an indication of feed quality. Considering the popularity of ammoniation, it is imperative to establish a standard suitable for estimating treated straw quality.

ANIMAL EXPERIMENTS WITH AMMONIATED STRAW

Feeding experiments with beef cattle

A UNDP-funded project, *Beef cattle production system based on ammoniated straw*, was effected between 1991-1992 in Huaiyang and Shangshiu counties of Henan Province; Boxiang county in Hebei Province, and some other regions. At the same time, beef cattle feeding experiments were conducted.

Experiments in Huaiyang county

Experiments were conducted in more than 100 counties with 259 animals. Cattle had *ad libitum* access to ammoniated straw and received a concentrate supplement according to body weight. Each animal needed 0.5 to 2.25 kg of concentrate feed (3/4 cotton seed cake + 1/4 maize grain). Results of feeding experiments are presented in Table 3-3, and the economic benefits in Table 3-4.

Results showed that average daily gain between 150 and 450 kg was 0.5 kg. The ratio of concentrate to weight gain was in the range of 0.83 to 3.5. This ratio was less than 2 for cattle under 350 kg. It took 498 days to go from 150 to 450 kg. Experiments with calves were also conducted. The results demonstrated that it took less than 2.5 years from birth to market weight (450 kg) under the current management regime. It took less than 2 years to bring cattle to 400 kg.

Table 3-3. Feeding experiments with ammoniated straw in Huaiyang county

Body weight (kg)	Concentrate (kg/day)	Straw intake (kg/day)	Weight gain (g/day)	Concentrate per kg gained
151 – 200	0.5	5.2	605	0.83
201 – 250	0.7	6.0	574	1.22
251 – 300	0.9	6.6	593	1.52
301 – 350	1.3	7.1	654	1.99
351 – 400	1.8	7.4	514	3.50
401 – 450	2.3	7.9	707	3.18

Table 3-4. Economic analysis from studies in Huaiyang county

Body weight (kg)	Weight gain (g/day)	Inputs (¥/day)	Output (¥/day)	Benefit (¥/day)
151 – 200	605	0.78	2.30	1.52
201 – 250	574	0.94	2.18	1.24
251 – 300	593	1.08	2.25	1.17
301 – 350	654	1.30	2.48	1.18
351 – 400	514	1.53	1.95	0.42
401 – 450	707	1.77	2.69	0.92

NOTES: Feed prices: cotton seed cake, ¥ 0.4/kg; maize, ¥ 0.5/kg; urea, ¥ 1.0/kg; wheat straw, ¥ 0.04/kg. Depreciation of feeding equipment and health care were ¥ 0.1/head/day. Cattle price was ¥ 3.8/kg. Worker labour costs were covered by manure sales.

Experiments in Shangshui County

The experiments were carried out on 85 private farmers, with 344 cattle, during 1992. Cattle had free access to ammoniated straw mixed with concentrate according to body weight. Each beast consumed 1.5 to 2 kg concentrate (3/4 cotton seed cake + 1/4 ground maize) per day. The results of feeding experiments are shown in Table 3-5, and the economic benefits in Table 3-6.

Average daily gain was between 608 and 629 g from 150 to 450 kg when cattle consumed ammoniated straw supplemented with 1.5-2 kg concentrate per day. The ratio of concentrate to weight gain was 2.39-3.29. It took 482 days from 150 to 450 kg, with a daily average input of ¥ 1.31, an output of ¥ 2.36 and net profit of ¥ 506.1 per animal.

Table 3-5. Feeding experiments with ammoniated straw in Shangshui county

Body weight (kg)	Concentrate (g/day)	Straw intake (kg/day)	Weight gain (g/day)	Concentrate per kg of gain
150 - 250	1.5	7.0	628	2.39
251 - 350	2.0	8.9	629	3.18
351 - 450	2.0	11.4	608	3.29

Table 3-6. Economic analysis of studies in Shangshui county

Body weight (kg)	Weight gain (g/day)	Inputs (¥/day)	Output (¥/day)	Benefit (¥/day)
150 - 250	628	1.05	2.39	1.34
251 - 350	629	1.38	2.39	1.01
351 - 450	608	1.50	2.31	0.81

NOTES: Feed prices: cottonseed cake, ¥ 0.4/kg; maize grain, ¥ 0.5/kg; urea, ¥ 1.0/kg; wheat straw, ¥ 0.04/kg. Depreciation of feeding equipment and health care were ¥ 0.1/head/day. The price of live cattle was ¥ 3.8/kg.

Studies by Institute of Animal Production and Health in Hebei Province

Twelve 18-month-old cattle were divided into 4 groups receiving *ad libitum* four straw sources: wheat straw, maize stover, ammoniated wheat straw and ammoniated maize stover. In addition, each animal received 1.5 kg of cotton seed cake per day. The study lasted 80 days, starting 21 February 1992. The results are presented in Table 3-7.

The results confirmed that gains were better with ammoniated straw. Treatment of wheat straw improved growth 85.1 percent (from 348 to 644 g/day) and treatment of maize stover by 45 percent (from 513 to 744 g/day). It also reduced the concentrate needed per kg of gain (from 4.32 to 2.33 kg). In other words, 1.99 kg concentrate was saved and straw conversion rate increased by 46.1 percent. Corresponding figures for maize stover were 2.93 to 2.02 kg of concentrate needed per kg gain; 0.91 kg of concentrate saved; and conversion improvement of 31.1 percent. Intake of crop residue DM varied from 2.14 to 2.83 kg per 100 kg of weight. Intake order was: ammoniated maize stover > maize stover > ammoniated wheat straw > wheat straw.

Table 3-7. Results of feeding experiments in Hebei Province

		Group			
		Untreated wheat straw	Untreated maize stover	Ammoniated wheat straw	Ammoniated maize straw
Number of cattle		3	3	3	3
Days of experiment		80	80	80	80
Average initial weight	(kg)	234.8	234.8	234.8	234.8
Total weight gained	(kg)	83.4	122.8	154.5	178.6
Average gain	(g/day)	348	513	644	744
Cottonseed intake	(kg/day)	1.5	1.5	1.5	1.5
Total feed intake	(% BW)	2.56	3.10	2.94	3.29
Straw intake	(% BW)	2.14	2.70	2.48	2.83
Concentrate:gain ratio		4.32	2.93	2.33	2.02
Straw degradation rate	(%)	45.03	62.97	54.75	69.31

Experiments in Dingxing County

Experiments were carried out on demonstration farms. Thirty local yellow cattle of 200 to 300 kg BW and 1.5 to 2 years old were selected and divided into 3 groups. Cattle were mainly fed *ad libitum* with ammoniated wheat straw (treated with 5 percent urea). The groups were supplied with 2, 3 and 4 kg cottonseed cake, respectively, to study the effect of supplement level. The experiments started on 26 May 1992 and lasted 42 days. Results are presented in Table 3-8.

Results showed that daily gains increased with concentrate level, but in a diminishing response. From 2 to 3 kg, gains increased by 217 g/day, or 22.5 percent, but from 3 to 4 kg, only by 105 g/day, or 14.1 percent. The efficiency of concentrate use for growth also decreased with the level.

The results from the above studies show that on the basis of ammoniated straw diets, the concentrate required per kg of weight gain varied from 0.83 to 3.5 kg, starting at 150 kg. The concentrate used per kg of liveweight gain was less in cattle than in swine. Cattle market age can be reduced to 2.5 years. This low-level concentrate feeding system is well suited for Chinese conditions.

Table 3-8. Effects of cottonseed cake ration on daily gain

		Group		
		I	II	III
Number of cattle		10	10	10
Experimental period	(days)	42	42	42
Cottonseed cake intake	(kg/day)	2	3	4
Ammoniated straw intake	(kg/day)	7.25	7	4
Total initial group weight	(kg)	2 629	2532	2 847
Total final group weight	(kg)	2 885	2943	3 205
Total weight gain	(kg)	256	312	358
Average daily gain	(g/day)	609	826	931
Concentrate to gain ratio		3.28:1	4.04:1	4.70:1
Straw to gain ratio		11.89:1	9.44:1	7.93:1
Cost of gain	(¥/kg)	2.94	2.97	3.11
Total income	(¥)	922	1 121	1 287
Total expenses	(¥)	528	718	911
Net benefit per head	(¥)	39.4	40.4	37.6

Feeding dairy cows

The Rowett Research Institute of UK reported the use of ammoniated straw for dairy cows instead of dry hay, without effects on milk yield or quality. Most researchers have tried ammoniated straw feeding for beef cattle and growing cattle, but there have been very few studies on high yielding dairy cows (> 7 000 kg/lactation). In 1999, Lu Xilei from the Beijing Dairy Institute conducted systematic experiments feeding high production cows with ammoniated straw, with great success. Some results are presented here.

Feeding dairy cows with ammoniated rice straw (1990)

Ammoniated rice straw replaced 30 percent of Chinese wild-rye hay in the ration, without negative effects on yield and composition (Tables 3-9 & 3-10).

Table 3-9. Groups of dairy cattle for ammoniated rice straw study

Group	$n^{(1)}$	Number of calvings	Milking days	Milk production (kg/day)	Body weight (kg)
Treated straw	30	2.7	167	24.1	573
Untreated straw	30	2.8	164	23.6	576
P		> 0.05	> 0.05	> 0.05	> 0.05

NOTE: (1) Number of dairy cows in each group

Table 3-10. Average milk production and composition when feeding rice straw

Group	$n^{(1)}$	Days	Milk production (kg)	Fat (%)	Protein (%)	Lactose (%)
Treated straw	30	112	24.12	3.24	-	4.75
Untreated straw	30	112	23.39	3.51	3.19	4.80
P			>0.05	>0.05	>0.05	>0.05

NOTE: (1) Number of dairy cows in each group

Feeding dairy cows with ammoniated maize straw (1991)

Feeding experiments were carried out supplying half of the ration as either ammoniated maize stover (group A) or untreated maize stover (group B). The other half was Chinese wild-rye hay. A third group (C) received only Chinese wild-rye hay. The comparisons of milk yield and composition among the three groups are shown in Table 3-11. No negative effects on milk production and composition were found when ammoniated maize stover or untreated maize stover substituted half of the Chinese wild-rye hay, but obvious economic profits were obtained. In other words, ammoniated straw could replace part of Chinese wild-rye hay for high yielding cows (with 7 500 kg of milk per lactation), but whether it could be replaced completely still needs further experimentation. A Shuangqiao farmer obtained good results with total replacement of Chinese wild-rye hay by ammoniated straw.

Table 3-11. Comparison of milk production and composition among three groups

Group	n[(1)]	Milk yield (kg)	Fat (%)	Protein (%)	Lactose (%)
A	6	26.24	3.30	2.94	4.73
B	6	25.48	3.20	3.01	4.75
C	6	25.27	3.30	3.06	4.82
P		>0.05	>0.05	>0.05	>0.05

NOTE: (1) Number of dairy cows in each group

Feeding sheep

In Norway, Nedkvitne and Maurtvedt (1980) conducted an experiment with pregnant ewes, feeding them with straw and concentrates. One group was fed with 0.6-0.8 kg forage and another with 0.8-1.0 kg ammoniated straw. Mean values of the 3-year experiment are shown in Table 3-12.

Results showed that there was no obvious difference in the number of lambs born between the two groups. Weight increases during pregnancy for the ammoniated straw group were more rapid than in the untreated group, but weight losses were also greater, so weight balance was better with forage. There were no differences in lamb weight in autumn.

In recent years, some institutes in China have also used ammoniated straw in feeding experiments. For example, Zhen Erying from Hebei Agricultural University used urea-treated rice straw to feed sheep, with satisfactory results.

Table 3-12. Results of feeding ammoniated straw to pregnant ewes

Parameter		Forage group	Ammonia straw group
Feedstuffs	(kg/day)		
Forage		0.6 - 0.8	–
Ammoniated straw		–	0.8 – 1.0
Silage		1.5 - 2.5	1.5 – 2.5
Concentrate		0.2 - 0.3	0.2 – 0.3
Lambs per lambing		54/31	45/34
Ewe weight on 12 December	(kg)	74	75
Weight gain during pregnancy	(kg)	8.7	10.7
Net weight gain after lambing	(kg)	2.7	1.0
Lamb birth weight	(kg)	5.1	5.1
Lamb weight gain in spring	(g/day)	344	344
Lamb weight in autumn	(kg)	49	49

SOURCE: Unpublished report (1991) on dairy cows fed on ammonia-treated residues. Shuangqiao State Farm, Beijing.

Chapter 4

Ensiling crop residues

Liu Jianxin
Zhejiang University
Guo Jun
China National Breeding Stock
Import and Export Corporation

Silage is the material produced by controlled fermentation of crop residues or forages with high moisture content. The purpose is to preserve forages by natural fermentation by achieving anaerobic conditions and discouraging clostridial growth. The ideal characteristics of material for silage preservation are: an adequate level of fermentable substrate (8-10 percent of DM) in the form of water soluble carbohydrate (WSC); a relatively low buffering capacity; and a DM content above 200 g/kg. The ensiling material should also ideally have, after harvesting and chopping, a physical form that allows easy compaction in the silo. Materials such as maize stover and grass can be ensiled successfully, while crop residues such as rice and wheat straw, with low WSC content, do not fulfil these requirements, and therefore pre-treatments, such as fine chopping or use of additives, or both, may be necessary.

There are plenty of materials suitable for ensilage in China. Whole maize and stover are the most common materials. Sweet potato vines are also usually ensiled after harvesting the tubers. In the provinces along the Yangtze River valley, large amounts of Chinese milk vetch are cultivated as green manure to improve soil fertility. Traditionally, farmers ensile surplus vetch for later use.

TYPES OF SILOS

Tower silo

In China, tower silos are constructed from brick, and are several metres in diameter and 10-20 m in height. The advantages of this type of silo include: long life, small space required, low storage losses, and possibility for mechanization. Both the filling operation and daily extraction can be mechanized. However, tower silos are expensive, and therefore not widely used in China, with the exception of some state-owned farms.

Cellar silo

The cellar type is the most common silo on individual farms. Round or square concrete silos are usually built inside houses for protection from the weather. Advantages are lower cost and easy management. Size can be adjusted according to scale of production. Cellar silos are suitable for rural conditions in China. A disadvantage is high effluent loss, especially with clay walls.

Trench silo

This type is generally built underground or semi-underground, with two solid walls of 1.5-2 m in height. Advantages are similar to the cellar silo, but the trench silo is more suitable for mechanization. The tractor can be driven on top from one side to the other for compaction purposes. After compaction, it is covered with a plastic sheet pressed down with soil, sandbags or straw bales to maintain anaerobic conditions.

On many dairy farms, trench silos are built on the surface of ground. This type of trench silo resembles a bunker silo, but has vertical walls of 0.4-0.5 m in thickness and 3-4 m in height. This design makes mechanization more convenient, and may also prevent bottom leakage.

Stack silo

This type of silo implies a pile of material on the ground surface. On flat and dry ground, plastic sheet is placed underneath and the material is laid in a stack. The top is covered with plastic and sealed all round with soil. Sandbags or old tyres, or any other suitable objects, are placed on top to prevent the top cover from being blown away by the wind. The advantages of the stack silo are low cost and flexibility of placement.

Plate 4-1. Ensiling, building a trench on the ground

Plate 4-2. Ensiling, building a trench below ground surface

Plate 4-3. Silage bales wrapped with plastic

Plate 4-4. Tower silos, Shanxi, China

Plastic silo

Animal scientists from Neijiang, Sichuan Province, successfully ensiled sweet potato vines in plastic bags in 1978. The plastic silo is similar to the stack silo but it is covered with plastic sheets of polyvinyl chloride (PVC) or polyethylene. Alternately, the silo can be made in bags with sealed tops. The stack silo is also inexpensive and can be placed anywhere. However, labour requirements are high due to manual filling and handling. A specific machine has recently been developed by the Grassland Institute, Chinese Academy of Agricultural Science, to fill plastic bags with forage.

SILAGE MAKING

Control of moisture content in raw materials

Ensilage can only be successful, with minimum DM and nutrient losses, when the moisture content of the raw material is kept to a suitable level. Although silage may be made within a large range of moisture contents, DM should be over 20 percent to assure silage quality.

There are many disadvantages to ensiling crops with high moisture content. First, ensiling of wet materials results in the generation of a large volume of effluent, which not only poses disposal problems, but also carries off valuable, highly digestible nutrients in solution. The amount of effluent increases with silo height, due to pressure. Effluent is produced when moisture is above 75 percent. Secondly, the critical pH value for clostridial growth varies directly with the moisture content of the plant material, and unless soluble carbohydrate levels are exceptionally high, ensiling wet crops will encourage clostridial fermentation, resulting in high losses and reduced nutritive value. Thirdly, even if the water-soluble carbohydrate (WSC) levels are adequate to ensure lactic fermentation, very wet silages may still be nutritionally undesirable because voluntary DM intake of these is frequently low. Finally, drier plant materials are preferred because they are easier to handle and a higher quantity of DM can be carried per trailer load.

Moisture content of forage and grasses is above 80 percent when harvested at a suitable stage. Therefore the moisture content should be reduced by field wilting. It takes 4 to 6 hours to wilt in dry regions such as the northwestern provinces and Inner Mongolia, and 6 to 10 hours in northeastern and northern areas. Longer periods may be needed in southern provinces, depending on climate and weather, but it is not desirable to exceed 24 hours. When weather conditions are unfavourable, field wilting should be avoided to prevent nutrient loss due to rain leaching. In these cases, other methods should be considered.

In contrast, the moisture content of cereal straw is generally too low to allow tight packing, so cereal straw and stover should be finely chopped. Sometimes water should be added to bring moisture content to a suitable level.

Sweet potato vines are high in moisture content and wilting is necessary. Chopped vines are usually mixed with finely chopped straw or bran prior to ensiling to increase overall DM content.

The moisture content of plant materials may be measured with instruments, but it is usually estimated manually on farm. Samples of chopped and minced grass or leguminous forage are grasped tightly by hand for one minute or so to estimate moisture content. If juice can be extracted, moisture content is above 75 percent. If the material remains together but without juice, moisture content is between 70-75 percent. If the material has elasticity and spreads out slowly, moisture content is 55-65 percent. If the material spreads out quickly, moisture content is about 55 percent. If the material breaks, moisture content may be below 55 percent.

Chopping, compaction and sealing

Prior to ensiling, plant materials should be chopped. The fineness of chopping varies with moisture content and nature of the material. The following guidelines can be used, but, in principle, rough and hard materials should be finely chopped, while delicate and soft materials can be roughly chopped.

High moisture forage (Moisture >75%)	chop to 6.5-25 mm
Wilted materials (Moisture 60-70%)	chop to 6.5 mm
Whole maize plant	chop to 6.5-13 mm

What are the advantages of chopping? Firstly, chopping facilitates compaction and thus reaching the anaerobic stage. When most oxygen is removed, clostridial growth is discouraged and lactic acid fermentation encouraged. Secondly, chopping releases plant juices, stimulating the growth of lactic acid bacteria. Thirdly, chopping may increase silage intake by improving quality of fermentation and by accelerating rate of passage of feed particles through the rumen. However, very finely chopped silage reduces the rumination and may decrease milk fat content. Thus, 10-15 percent of the silage material should be above 25 mm in length in order to maintain an effective fibre function.

Factors influencing silage quality

Quality of silage fermentation is influenced by several factors, including moisture, WSC content of raw materials, degree of compaction and effectiveness of final sealing. Stage of maturity influences a forage's nutritive value and thus quality of silage. Leguminous forages at budding stage have optimal energy, protein and carotene contents, but DM yield and nutritive value decrease with maturity (Table 4-1). Grass at heading stage is highest in caloric value and protein content. When leguminous forages reach late flowering stage or grasses reach seed stage, the energy value has decreased by 70-75 percent, digestible CP by 67-83 percent, and carotene content by 75-84 percent.

Table 4-1. Yield of dry matter and nutrients in legumes and grasses by growth stage

Growth stage	Yield (ton/ha)			
	Fresh yield	DM	Feed unit	Digestible CP
Legumes				
Pre-bud	13.0	2.7	2.3	0.44
Mid-bud	16.5	4.2	3.8	0.58
Flowering	14.8	4.2	3.7	0.54
Full bloom	8.4	3.5	1.9	0.19
Green seed pod	7.1	2.8	1.2	0.13
Milky ripe and dough seed	6.8	2.8	0.5	0.10
Grasses				
Heading	17.2	5.0	4.6	0.49
Early bloom	17.3	5.2	3.8	0.40
Full bloom	9.1	3.8	2.3	0.19
Green seed pod	8.4	3.0	1.2	0.08
Milky ripe	8.0	3.0	1.1	0.06
Dough seed	7.8	2.6	0.7	0.05

Therefore, it is important to harvest forage crops at their optimal stages. Legumes should be harvested at budding stage, grasses at heading stage, and whole maize plant at late milky to early dough seed stage.

Grass is highest in protein at pre-heading, and highest energetically at dough seed stage. Many grasses can not head again after the first cutting, and the regrowth may be collected 4 to 5 weeks after the first harvest. The appropriate stages at which plants may be harvested are indicated in Table 4-2.

Table 4-2. Appropriate harvest stages for grasses and forage crops

Grass and forage crops	Stage of growth	Moisture (%)
Alfalfa	Late bud to 1/10 bloom	70-80
Red clover	Late bud to early bloom	75-82
Orchard grass	Pre-head to heading	
Awnless bromegrass	Pre-head to heading	75
Timothy	Pre-head to heading	
Sudan grass	About 90 cm in height	80
Mixed grasses	Pre-head to early heading	
Mixed legume and grass	Depending on grass	
Grain forage	Pre-head to early heading	
Whole-crop maize	Dough seed	65-70
Maize stover	Soonest after maize harvest	50-60
Whole-crop sorghum	Early to mid-dough seed	70
Sorghum stover	Soonest after sorghum harvest	60-70
Oat	Pre-head to early heading	82
Oat	Milky ripe	78
Oat	Early dough seed	70
Barley	Late bud to early dough seed	82-70
Rye	Late bud to early dough seed	80-75

Because straw and stover are harvested after grain collection, their nutritional value is generally low. It has been recently shown that yield and grain quality do not change when harvest is shifted to an earlier stage (by 7-10 days). However, this shift may be beneficial in terms of improved nutritional value of straw and stover.

SILAGE ADDITIVES

The purpose of using additives is to ensure silage quality by encouraging lactic acid fermentation, by inhibiting undesirable microbes or by improving its nutritional value. Common silage additives include bacterial cultures, acids, inhibitors of aerobic damage, and nutrients.

Bacterial cultures

A dominant lactic acid fermentation is the key to making good silage. Lactic acid bacteria are normally present on harvested crops together with clostridial bacteria in a ratio of about 10 to 1. Considerable nutrient loss usually occurs at initial stages of ensiling when oxygen is still present. Addition of lactic acid bacterial cultures during filling-up increases their population rapidly, encouraging lactic acid fermentation and pH reduction to a level that inhibits clostridial development. Different strains of lactic acid bacteria look similar under the microscope, but their biological activities are very different. Only those acid-tolerant strains that possess a homo-fermentative pathway, producing the maximum amount of lactic acid from hexose sugars readily available, and a growth temperature range extending to 50°C, should be used as a silage additive.

The environment under which lactic acid bacteria multiply favourably is also important. Lactic acid bacteria are anaerobic, and hence air should be removed and the silo should be kept airtight. These micro-organisms ferment soluble sugars to a mixture of acids, but predominantly lactic acid. Plant materials should contain at least 2 percent WSC, otherwise soluble sugars (e.g. molasses) should be added. Starch may also be added along with amylase in order to provide lactic acid bacteria with soluble sugars.

Cereal straws and stovers are high in lignocellulose. A mixture of inoculum or enzymes, or both, containing cellulase and xylanase is often used. Enzymes degrade lignocellulose, liberating soluble sugars for bacterial use. A number of commercial preparations are available from foreign companies, and some have been registered by government authorities and can be sold in China. During the Ninth Five-Year Plan, Chinese scientists successful produced a special additive for ensiling fresh cereal straws and stovers.

Mineral or organic acids

The original proposal to use acids as silage additives dates back to 1885. In the late 1920s, Virtanen from Finland, adopted this approach and recommended the rapid acidification of the crop with mineral acids (AIV process) to a pH of about 3.5, which was originally thought to inhibit microbial and plant enzyme activity. This AIV process was widely used in Scandinavia until quite recently. Due to the difficulties in handling corrosive acids, organic acids were later used as silage additives. When acids are added, plant materials sink quickly and are easy to consolidate. Acidity may arrest plant respiration and reduce heat production and nutrient loss. Rapid acidification may also inhibit clostridia. However, addition of acids increases effluent and can be potentially toxic to animals. Furthermore, acids are corrosive to people, animals and machinery. Reduction of moisture content may minimize effluent, and addition of calcium carbonate can be used to adjust silage acidity. Appropriate concentrations of different acids as silage additives are recommended as follows:

- sulphuric and hydrochloric acids: 50-80 litre of dilute acid (concentrated acid diluted with water at 1:5 v/v) per tonne
- formic acid: about 3 kg/ton
- acetic acid: 5-20 kg/ton
- propionic acid: 1 litre/m^2 of surface to prevent mould development.

Inhibitors of aerobic deterioration
The most common inhibitors of aerobic deterioration are sodium nitrate, sodium nitrite, sodium formate and formaldehyde. These chemicals do not contribute to the improvement of fermentation, but are effective in preventing silage deterioration. Some plant parts, such as larch leaves, contain natural bactericides that may safely function as antiseptics. Formaldehyde is a well-known sterilizing agent and is commercially available as formalin, which contains 40 percent of the gas in aqueous solution. Scientists are interested in the additives because of their bacteriostatic properties, and because of their known properties of protecting plant proteins from rumen microbial degradation. Adding formaldehyde at 3-15 kg/ton may result in a well-preserved silage.

Nutrients
Nutrient additives are defined as substances which, when added to ensilage materials, contribute significantly to the nutritional value of the silage. Most of nutrient additives can also favour lactic acid fermentation. A number of materials are considered to be in this category.

Nitrogenous compounds
Certain crops, such as maize and most cereal straw, are nutritionally deficient in nitrogen, and when fed to ruminants as silage require supplementing with a protein supplement. An alternative approach is to improve the CP content of the silage by adding urea during ensiling. When applied to maize, urea produces

silages with higher pH values and fermentation acid contents than in untreated silages. Urea addition has also a marked effect on nitrogenous components of the silages, resulting in higher CP, true protein, free amino acids and ammonia. Addition of urea to cereal straw and stover may also have an ammoniation effect, which is associated with higher CP and lower fibre content. However, attention should be paid to the rapid release of ammonia from urea in the rumen. High concentrations of ammonia in the rumen may cause ammonia poisoning. One solution is to add the urea or other nitrogenous compounds together with soluble sugar sources, such as molasses and starchy grains.

Urea may be added at 0.5 percent of fresh materials. When whole maize plant was added with urea at 0.5 percent, the CP of the resulting silage increased to 12.9 from 8.7 percent in the untreated silage. Urea may also be added prior to feeding the animals.

Carbohydrate-rich materials
Carbohydrate-rich materials are added to silage crops in order to increase the supply of available energy for the growth of lactic acid bacteria, and are of particular importance in crops such as legumes, which are deficient in soluble carbohydrate content. Materials that have been used for this purpose include molasses and cereals. Molasses is a by-product of the sugar industry, and has a DM content of 70-75 percent and a soluble carbohydrate content of about 65 percent of DM. In order to obtain maximum benefit, it should be used at 4 percent (w/w) for grass silage and 6 percent (w/w) for legume silage. Cereals have been used as additives in an attempt to improve both the fermentation quality and the nutritional value of silages. Cereals contain 50-55 percent of starch that can be hydrolysed to soluble sugars and then utilized by lactic acid bacteria. If amylase or amylase-rich materials, such as malt, are added with the cereal to ensiled crops, they will be more effective as fermentable carbohydrate sources.

Minerals
In addition to being nutritionally deficient in N, most straw and stover is a poor source of Ca and many micro-elements. Limestone is sometimes added to silages as Ca supplement and to alleviate silage acidity. Calcium carbonate may be added at 0.45-0.50 percent to obtain maximum benefit. Common salt has a high osmotic pressure to which clostridia are sensitive, but lactic acid bacteria

are not. Addition of salt may increase lactate content, decrease acetate and butyrate, resulting in silage with good quality and palatability.

Other minerals may be used in ensiled materials. Examples of mineral sources include copper sulphate (2.5 ppm), manganese sulphate (5 ppm), zinc sulphate (2 ppm), cobalt chloride (1 ppm) and potassium iodide (0.1 ppm).

Finally, it has to be pointed out that recommendations on the use of silage additives must be based not only on the results of scientific research, but also on sound economic return.

EVALUATION OF SILAGE QUALITY

The nutritive value and the quality of silage should be accurately evaluated. Working on behalf of the Bureau of Animal Production and Health (BAPH), MOA, researchers at Zhejiang University drafted methods of evaluating nutritive value and quality of silage, which have been tested in China since 1996. This handbook includes subjective methods (on-farm) and chemical methods (for use in laboratory).

Subjective methods of evaluation

The pH value and certain simple subjective criteria such as colour, smell and texture are used to evaluate the quality of silage on-farm. These criteria are briefly reviewed below.

pH value

The pH is the simplest and quickest way of evaluating silage quality, and may be determined on-farm using wide-range pH test papers such as bromophenol blue (range 2.8-4.4), bromocresol green (range 4.2-5.6) and methyl red (range 5.4-7.0). The classification of silage based on pH value is:

pH below 4.0	excellent
pH between 4.1 and 4.3	good
pH between 4.4 and 5.0	average
pH above 5.0	bad

production. However, the limited reports indicate that dairy cows perform well when they consume ammoniated straw.

Li and Wu (1991) compared straw intake and milk production in dairy cows given either untreated or anhydrous-ammonia-treated rice straw. Daily intake was 4.58 and 6.24 kg, and daily milk production 13.6 or 16.0 kg for untreated or ammoniated straw, respectively. In a trial with the ammonium-bicarbonate-treated rice straw, Liu *et al.* (1991b) found that 17-19 kg of milk could be obtained from Holstein cows when the ammoniated straw represented half of the intake (85 percent of roughage). These results were consistent with those of Ørskov (1987), where daily milk yield was 23.5-27.4 kg when ammoniated straw, as the sole roughage, was 35-60 percent of the diet.

It can be concluded that ammoniated straw is a good source of roughage for dairy cows, completely or partially substituting hay. However, it is certainly advisable to use other roughage sources in order to ensure a complete diet.

SUPPLEMENTATION WITH CONCENTRATE AND PROTEIN

The first constraint for low quality crop residue use is usually N. It is desirable that supplementation ensures an almost continuous supply of ammonia-N. Urea is commonly used as a source of fermentable N, and can be sprayed on cereal straw or be mixed with energy supplements. At present, non-protein N supplements have not been widely fed by farmers in China, but urea is usually used as a source of ammonia to upgrade crop residues. With the development of animal production based on crop residues, ammoniation of cereal straw has been widely extended all over China (Guo, 1996).

Since fermentable N is not limiting in ammoniated straw diets, greater consideration should be given to rumen-protected amino acids. They may overcome specific deficiencies limiting production or may be catabolized to improve the supply of glucogenic substrates, which are also usually insufficient in straw-based diets (Preston, 1995). Protein supplements used in China are mainly oilseed cakes or meals, such as cottonseed cake (CSC) and rapeseed meal (RSM). Sometimes farmers provide their animals with by-products such as rice and wheat bran, or home-grown or self-mixed concentrate mixtures.

Feeding and individual supplementation

Effectiveness of protein supplementation

Typical data on animal performance is given in Table 5-2. In Henan Province, an experiment with 40 young Chinese Yellow bulls was conducted to investigate CSC supplementation levels with urea-treated wheat straw (Zhang *et al.*, 1993). The cattle without CSC gained only 250 g/day, but with CSC gained significantly more (P <0.01). There were no significant differences between 2 and 3 kg, and between 3 and 4 kg of CSC, but there was between 1 and 2 kg. DM intake of wheat straw did not decrease when 1 kg CSC was supplemented, but it did at higher levels. The economic analysis indicated that a relatively high level of production and the highest profit were obtained with 2 kg of CSC. Similar results were obtained in Hebei Province (Fan *et al.*, 1993; Ma *et al.*, 1990; Table 5-2). Supplementation with 0.25 kg CSC significantly improved feed utilization efficiency and feed efficiency (kg of feed DM/kg gain being reduced from 53 to 15). The group given 1.5-2.0 kg of CSC gained approximately 800 g/d, with only 8 kg feed consumed per kg gain. Further increases of CSC resulted in slightly faster gains at the expense of straw intake.

Table 5-2. Effects of supplementation with cottonseed cake (CSC) on performance of growing Yellow cattle fed untreated or urea-treated wheat straw

Straw type	Straw intake (kg DM/day)	CSC (kg/d)	Initial weight (kg)	Daily gain (g/day)	FCR[1]	Source
Urea-treated	5.0	0	182	250	19.6	
Urea-treated	5.1	1	183	602	9.9	
Urea-treated	4.5	2	183	704	8.9	Zhang and Yuan, 1993
Urea-treated	4.2	3	183	836	8.2	
Urea-treated	2.9	4	183	878	6.8	
Urea-treated	5.2	0	175.1	99	53	
Urea-treated	5.5	0.25	170.5	370	15	
Urea-treated	5.3	0.5	183.6	529	11	
Urea-treated	5.4	1.5	192.8	781	8.8	Fan *et al.*, 1993
Urea-treated	5.1	2.0	175.0	819	8.6	
Urea-treated	5.2	2.5	193.7	841	9.2	
Urea-treated	4.5	3.0	215.5	880	8.6	
Urea-treated	3.6	4.0	213.5	904	8.6	
Untreated	4.3	0.5	187	100	44.3	
Untreated	4.9	1.0	194	240	20.6	Ma *et al.*, 1990
Urea-treated	4.8	0.5	198	485	10.8	
Urea-treated	4.3	1.0	213	660	8.0	

NOTE: (1) FCR = feed conversion ratio

Formaldehyde treatment was effective in improving protein use efficiency of RSM. In terms of nutrient digestibility and N use, formaldehyde-treated RSM compares favourably with treated soybean meal when given to sheep fed ammoniated rice straw (Liu *et al.*, 1994). When an ammoniated rice straw-based diet was supplemented with 1.2 kg RSM, heifers had lower weight gains, whereas feeding a similar level of treated RSM resulted in considerably faster gains (15 percent on average) along with improved feed conversion ratio (FCR) and decreased feed cost (Liu *et al.*, 1993) (Table 5-3). This was also the case when 1.8 kg of RSM was given. Adverse effects on animal health are unlikely when formaldehyde-treated RSM is supplemented in an ammoniated rice straw based diet (Wu and Liu, unpublished data).

Table 5-3. Supplementation effects of untreated or formaldehyde-treated rapeseed meal (RSM) on weight gain of heifers

	Untreated RSM		Treated-RSM	
Amount (kg/day)	1.2	1.8	1.2	1.8
Number of animals	15	15	15	15
Initial weight (kg)	329	324	361	352
Liveweight gain (g/day)	491	556	564	665
Straw intake (kg/day)	5.0	5.0	5.0	5.0
Feed conversion ratio	13.5	12.9	11.6	10.6
Feed cost/kg gain (¥)	3.54	3.78	3.12	3.22

SOURCE: Liu *et al.*, 1993

Response of supplementation with untreated and treated straw

There are consistent responses in performance to supplementation with protein or concentrate, but the effects are more pronounced when the straw has been chemically treated.

Meng and Xiong (1993) studied the effect of supplementing with different levels of concentrate on growth rate of Wuzhumuqin wether lambs fed untreated or ammonia-treated wheat straw. Concentrate mixtures were chosen to obtain minimum feed cost per unit gain. The results are summarized in Table 5-4. Intake of both untreated and ammoniated straw diminished with increasing levels of concentrate, while animals consumed more ammoniated straw than untreated. Ammonia treatment increased straw DM intake on average by 72, 51, 57 and 117 percent, resulting in higher total DM intake for ammoniated straw diet. Treatment of wheat straw with ammonia resulted in a significant improvement in weight change of sheep and in feed conversion.

Supplementation with concentrate increased weight gain of wethers offered either untreated straw or the ammoniated, but the nature of the response differed according the type of straw. In order to obtain similar daily gains, larger amounts of concentrate were needed for untreated wheat straw than for ammoniated diets.

This indicates that benefits of ammoniation of straw are highest when the supplement level is low. The results show that minimum concentrate consumption per unit gain was obtained when the concentrate accounted for 45 percent of diet based on ammoniated wheat straw.

Table 5-4. Feed intake, digestibility and liveweight gain of sheep fed treated or untreated rice or wheat straw plus different levels of supplement

Parameter		Treatment group				Source
		1	2	3	4	
Level of concentrate [3]	(kg/day)	200	400	600	800	
Untreated wheat straw intake	(g/day)	353	325	271	149	
Total intake	(g/day)	545	698	821	852	
Liveweight gain	(g/day)	-9.8	35.1	63.6	103.7	
Concentrate/gain	(kg/kg)	-	12.0	8.9	6.9	Meng *et al.*,
Level of concentrate. [3]	(kg/day)	200	400	600	800	1993 [1]
Treated wheat straw intake	(g/day)	608	490	425	323	
Total intake	(g/day)	809	863	956	1038	
Liveweight gain	(g/day)	35.6	85.2	87.2	109.0	
Concentrate/gain	(kg/kg)	5.5	4.4	6.1	5.7	
Rice straw intake	(g/day)	432	404	406	343	
Rapeseed meal intake	(g/day)	0	88	175	263	
Total intake [4]	(g/day)	520	580	669	694	
Liveweight gain	(g/day)	-19	15	69	67	Liu *et al.*,
Ammoniated rice straw intake	(g/day)	566	562	541	431	1998 [2]
Rapeseed meal intake	(g/day)	0	88	175	263	
Total intake [4]	(g/day)	653	738	804	782	
Liveweight gain	(g/day)	20	63	74	77	

NOTES: (1) Meng *et al.* (1993) worked with Wuzhumuqin wethers (mean weight of 30.2 kg). (2) Liu *et al.* (1998) worked with Huzhou lambs (mean weight of 21 kg). (3) Ingredients: 82-86% maize meal; 11.5-11.8% CSC; 0-4.2% bone meal; 0.5-1.6% lime; 0.4-1.5% salt; and 0.2-0.8% mineral-vitamin premix. (4) Including 100 g of rice bran (DMI = 88 g/day).

Similar results were reported by Liu *et al.* (1998) (Table 5-4), with RSM as a supplement for Huzhou lambs offered untreated or ammoniated rice straw. The optimum level of RSM with ammoniated rice straw was 100 g/day, whereas 200 g/day had to be supplied to obtain the same liveweight gain with untreated straw. At existing prices (RSM at ¥ 1.50/kg, rice straw at ¥ 0.22/kg, and ammoniated straw at ¥ 0.27/kg), there is a benefit of ¥ 0.08/day from ammoniation, equivalent to ¥ 7.20/sheep for the normal 90-day fattening period.

SUPPLEMENTATION WITH GREEN FORAGES AND READILY DIGESTIBLE FIBROUS FEEDS

It is known that small quantities green forage can improve the usage of straw diets. Thus, introducing forage supplements may be an alternative strategy for increasing nutrient intake and improving ruminant performance. A wide range of forage supplements is available in China, depending on location. These include green forage, crop by-products and aquatic weeds.

Effects of supplementation with green forage

Chinese milk vetch (*Astragalus sinicus* L.) is cultivated in South China as green manure to improve soil fertility. Farmers traditionally offer surplus vetch to swine after ensiling. Liu *et al.* (1997) and Ye *et al.* (1996) evaluated the effect of supplementing with milk vetch silage on growth rate of heifers and rumen function in sheep given ammoniated rice straw diets (Table 5-5). Intake of ammoniated straw by heifers was slightly decreased as the level of vetch silage went up. When the vetch silage represented 20 or 30 percent of diet, growth rate was significantly higher than in the non-supplemented group (P <0.05). The highest gain was obtained at the 20 percent level, when concentrate consumption per kilogram weight gain was lowest (1.25 kg) (Liu *et al.*, 1997).

The average ammonia-N level in the rumen increased with the increasing level of vetch silage (Ye *et al.*, 1996). However, there were small differences in pH value and volatile fatty acid profiles among all groups. Protozoa population tended to decrease more quickly with the supplement. The microbial protein concentrations in the rumen fluid was related to the levels of vetch silage and reached a peak at 20 percent, possibly associated with saponins present in milk vetch.

Liu *et al.* (2001) substituted RSM with mulberry (*Morus alba*) leaves as a supplement for Huzhou growing lambs fed ammoniated rice straw. Total substitution with mulberry leaves gave similar growth rates, but at lower cost than RSM. The authors concluded that mulberry leaves could be used to supplement ammoniated straw diets in place of RSM.

Forage supplement level would depend on the type used, availability and the cost relative to straw. A maximum of 20-25 percent of a diet seems suitable.

The substitution rate would increase with the level of supplement. A limitation in China is that supplementary forages are usually in short supply in most areas.

Supplementation with readily digestible fibre

Prerequisites for all ruminal digestive processes are development of digestive consortia and their adhesion to ingested feed particles. Any feeding strategies that enhance adhesion of rumen microbes to feed particles and improve fibrolytic activity may be beneficial to feed utilization.

Table 5-5. Feed intake and liveweight gain of heifers, and rumen function of sheep, given rice straw and different levels of Chinese milk vetch silage

Level of vetch silage (%)	0	10	20	30	SEM[1]
Feeding trial with heifers (Liu *et al.*, 1997)					
Number of animals (head)	8	8	8	8	
Intake (kg DM/day)					
Ammoniated straw	3.61	3.59	3.02	2.65	-
Milk vetch silage	-	0.49	0.98	1.53	-
Concentrate mixture	0.90	0.90	0.90	0.90	-
Total	4.50	5.00	4.90	5.10	-
Initial weight (kg)	179	175	180	182	8.7
Weight gain[2] (g/day)	588[b]	692[ab]	800[a]	777[a]	46.2
Feed conversion ratio (kg/kg)	7.65	7.23	6.13	6.56	-
Rumen measurements in sheep (Ye *et al.*, 1996)					
pH value	6.6	6.7	6.7	6.7	0.02
Ammonia-N[2] (mg/dl)	11.7[c]	14.2[b]	15.2[b]	17.0[a]	1.0
Total VFA (mmol/dl)	8.1	7.9	8.5	8.4	0.45
Protozoa diminution rate[3] (%)	14	30	35	31	0.11
Microbial protein concentration in the rumen liquids (mg/ml)	2.6	2.9	3.2	2.8	0.12

NOTES: (1) SEM = Standard Error of the Mean.
(2) Means with different superscripts differ significantly (P<0.05).
(3) Ratio of protozoa population before feeding to that at 6 hours post-feeding.

In a recent trial, Shi *et al.* (1997) studied the effect of added ammoniated rice straw on the growth rate of Holstein heifers receiving untreated rice straw. The results are summarized in Table 5-6. When half (w/w) of the untreated straw was replaced by ammoniated straw, heifers had significantly higher intake and gains, even slightly higher than those on ammoniated straw. A similar result was reported by Li *et al.* (1998), who compared the growth rate of cross-bred cattle offered ammoniated wheat straw or maize stover, either alone or in a 50:50 (w/w) combination (Table 5-6).

Table 5-6. Straw intake and growth of heifers fed rice straw plus various supplements or of cattle on ammoniated wheat straw, maize stover or a mixture

		Treatment			
		1	2	3	4
Heifers (Shi *et al.*, 1987) [1]					
Dry matter intake	(kg/day)				
Rice straw		2.46	1.86	-	
Ammoniated rice straw		-	2.07	3.55	
Concentrate mixture		0.86	0.86	0.86	
Brewers' grains		1.03	1.03	1.03	
Total		4.35	5.82	5.44	
Liveweight gain	(kg/day)	0.66	0.84	0.81	
Cattle (Li *et al.*, 1998) [2]					
Intake	(kg/day)				
Ammoniated wheat straw		3.84	7.41	-	
Maize stover		3.84	-	8.16	
Concentrate mixture		2.80	2.80	2.80	
Liveweight gain	(kg./day)	0.98	0.85	0.83	
Concentrate/gain	(kg/kg)	2.55	2.96	3.04	
Heifers (Liu *et al.*, 2000) [3]					
Dry matter intake	(kg/day)				
Ammoniated rice straw		2.61	2.31	2.01	1.75
Bamboo shoot shell (BSS)		0	0.38	0.77	1.15
Cotton seed meal		0.93	0.93	0.93	0.93
Total		3.54	3.62	2.71	3.83
Substitute rate [4]		-	0.79	0.78	0.75
Liveweight gain	(kg/day)	0.622	0.629	0.744	0.690

NOTES: (1) Shi *et al.* (1987) worked with heifers (344-353 kg). (2) Li *et al.* (1998) worked with cattle of 370 kg. (3) Liu *et al.* (2000) worked with heifers (139-141 kg). (4) Expressed as the depression in the intake of ammoniated rice straw produced by a unit increase in the BSS intake.

Bamboo cultivation is very popular in south China. Bamboo shoot shells (BSS) are the residue from industrial-scale processing of bamboo shoots, and represent a disposal problem because they have no use and can pollute the environment. Occasionally it has been observed that fresh BSS were palatable to cattle, their CP was 10-13 percent (on DM basis) and were easily degraded in the rumen, although neutral detergent fibre was high (65-70 percent on DM basis) (Wang, 1997). Considering BSS as a source of readily digestible fibre, Liu *et al.* (2000) observed the response in growth rate to supplementation in heifers given ammoniated rice straw. The results are summarized in Table 5-6.

Straw intake linearly decreased with the increasing level of BSS, but total dietary intake increased also (a substitution rate less than 1.0). Growth rate in heifers was improved significantly by the supplementation, and the optimum level was at 21 percent of total dietary intake.

It is inferred that supplementation with readily digestible fibre may improve utilization of basal diet and animal performance. However, further work is needed on this topic.

USE OF MULTINUTRIENT BLOCKS

Since the early 1980s, both production and utilization of multinutrient blocks (MNBs) as supplements for ruminant animals have increased considerably in developing countries (Sansoucy, 1995). With the development of ruminant production, much progress has been made and new technologies have been developed in the manufacturing of MNBs in China since they were introduced in the late 1980s.

MNB manufacture
Ingredients
The MNBs developed in China contain molasses, urea, minerals and proteins, with the aim of supplementing cereal straw with fermentable N, soluble carbohydrates, minerals and other nutrients. The main ingredients have been: ground maize; rice bran and wheat bran; rapeseed meal; solidifiers and binders (cement, clay, etc.); bone meal; and vitamin premix (Chen *et al.*, 1993a, b; Li *et al.*, 1995; Zou *et al.*, 1996; Gao *et al.*, 1999). Molasses, a source of easily fermentable carbohydrates and a binder, makes blocks highly palatable. It has been demonstrated that mixing urea with molasses greatly decreases the release of ammonia-N in the rumen. Mineral premix usually contains Ca, P and Na as well as micro-elements such as Fe, Cu, Mn, Zn, I, Se and Co (Liu *et al.*, 1995; Zhang *et al.*, 1999).

In a series of demonstration trials in Gansu Province, where the basic diet was composed of wheat straw and other stubble, Chen *et al.* (1993a, b) selected three formulas, for cows, heifers and calves (Table 5-7). Many workers used molasses as an ingredient for blocks (Li *et al.*, 1995; Yang *et al.*, 1996; Guan *et al.*, 1998). Liu *et al.* (1995) found a block formula without molasses, since molasses is expensive and in short supply in some regions.

Lime and cement have been commonly used as solidifiers and binders. Ordinary clay has been also proved to be efficient for making blocks (Chen *et al.*, 1993a, b; Guan *et al.*, 1998). Farmers in some regions used loess as a binder (H.W. Ye, personal communication).

Table 5-7. Formulas of multinutrient blocks for dairy cattle (on a percentage by weight basis)

Ingredients	Cow	Heifer	Calf
Molasses	8	10	15
Urea	16	12	–
Salt	26	26	22.8
Ground maize	5	5	10
Lime	10	10	10
Clay	11.2	15	15
Bone meal	–	–	5
Mineral mixture	23.8	22	22.2
Total	100	100	100

Process for block manufacture and specifications

Depending on the technical process, MNB preparation takes two forms: by pressure (hot process), or by moulding (cold process). The moulding process needs neither sophisticated equipment nor much energy. Blocks produced by moulding had the following features (Ma *et al.*, 1992): (1) When water was poured onto the surface of the blocks, blocks kept their shape after sun-drying; (2) Blocks maintained their shape intact when submerged in water for 1-2 hours, but completely dispersed after 4-5 hours; (3) Hardness increased when formaldehyde was included; (4) The shape of the blocks did not change under finger pressure.

Xia *et al.* (1994) developed a specialized machine to make blocks under pressure. This equipment saved space and labour, and the blocks could be easily produced. Drying was unnecessary since it used raw materials already dry. The blocks produced were compact, not deliquescent, and hard enough to control intake. They did not become mouldy nor did they lose shape when exposed to rain or sunshine.

Table 5-8 indicates the characteristics of two press machines for the formation of blocks, designed by Chen *et al.* (1993a, b). The blocks were made by mixing molasses and urea, and then heating. Salt was added, followed by the rest of the ingredients, having been previously mixed together. The complete mixture was then pressed and the resulting blocks were wrapped immediately. Blocks made using both press machines were hard enough, with a breaking strength of 44 kg/cm^2. The blocks were oblate, 25.6 cm in diameter and 8 cm in thickness, with a weight of 7.5 kg each.

Table 5-8. Characteristics of presses used for making the blocks

Press type	Power source	Dimensions (cm)	Weight (kg)	Working pressure (kg/cm^2)	Production capacity (kg/hour)
9YK-50 (manual)	Hydraulic jack (50 tonne)	60 × 70 × 100	240	52	50
9YK-150 (electric)	Hydraulic pump (0.75 kW)	75 × 40 × 200	640	176	150

The blocks produced by Yang *et al.* (1996) were squares or compressed cylindroids with rounded holes (ca 1.5 cm diameter) in the centre. Each block weighed 2.5 kg. The breaking strength was 56.9 kg/cm^2. They did not moisten before 24 hour under low temperature (> 0°C) and high humidity (> 80 percent).

The urea-mineral blocks designed by Liu *et al.* (1995) had a breaking strength of 40 kg/cm^2. They were easily transported and fed to the animals. Even in situations of high humidity, there were no losses from mould or from hydration when they were offered to the animals over a long period.

In 1999, MOA set up a "block expert group." Based on results of previous studies and six months of research, an industrial production technology system was proposed. The MOA appraised it, and confirmed it "in the national leading position." The blocks have sold very well.

Results of blocks with animals
Beef cattle
In a growth trial with heifers, those having access to MNBs had daily gains of 835 g/day, 112 g/day higher (P<0.05) than the control group (Chen *et al.*, 1993a, b). Animals supplemented with blocks reached 380 kg body weight (weight at

first service) 65 days earlier. Other advantages observed during animal feeding trials on farms were better skin coat, better body condition, and lower death rate. The urea-MNBs without molasses were also palatable to both cattle and goats (Liu *et al.*, 1995). Local Yellow cattle on grazings with access to blocks performed better than the control (370 vs 203 g/day). The animals with blocks had better body condition and looked healthier than the control group. An increased income of ¥ 0.57 could be obtained per beast per day.

Zhang *et al.* (1993) observed that daily gains were 15.6 percent higher, and consumption of roughage and concentrate per kilogram of gain were 16.9 and 13.3 percent lower, respectively, when beef cattle were supplemented with MNBs containing non-protein nitrogenous compounds (NPN). In another trial (Ma *et al.*, 1995), beef cattle with access to blocks containing NPN had daily gains 353 g higher than those with no blocks (1 478 vs 1 125 g/day).

Dairy cows

Dairy cows supplemented with MNBs produced 1.06-1.47 kg (5.3-5.9 percent) more milk than those without blocks (Wang *et al.*, 1995). Less metabolic disorders occurred in the supplemented animals. Increased net income attributed to the blocks was about ¥ 1 per cow per day. Chen *et al.* (1993a, b) found that cows having access to blocks had an average milk yield of 20.7 kg/day, which was 1.3 kg (6.7 percent) higher (P < 0.01) than the average of the control group. Additional advantages of blocks included increased conception rate (12.2 percent), decreased occurrence of diseases (22.5 percent), improved body condition (Chen *et al.*, 1992) and increased income.

Urea-MNBs was given to Holstein cows in mid lactation by Xu *et al.* (1993). Cows produced 20.5 kg of milk, which was 4.1 kg (25 percent) higher than the average of the control group. It was estimated that cows consuming the MNBs increased income by ¥ 736 per head per year.

Sheep and goats

Xu *et al.* (1994) observed increased intake and improved daily gain (26.5 percent) in sheep having access to MNBs, compared to control animals. They also produced better quality wool with higher S and mineral content. Similar results were observed by Yang *et al.* (1996).

When hybrid goats had access to urea-MNBs for two months, average intake of the blocks was 39.5 g/day (Huang *et al.*, 1999). Daily weight gain for goats was 85 with and 62 g/day without MNBs. Net income was increased by ¥ 10.78

with blocks. Liu *et al.* (1995) reported results with goats, which grazed on hill pasture during the day and were offered rice straw *ad libitum* in stalls at night. Goats with free access to urea-MNBs along with rice straw at night performed better than those in the control group. Gains were significantly higher in animals with blocks (95 vs 73 g/day). The effects of MNBs on performance of growing goats were investigated by Zhang *et al.* (1999). Goats with blocks had weight gains 38.3 percent higher than those without.

Buffaloes

Effects of feeding blocks to buffaloes have been observed by some workers (Lu *et al.*, 1995a; Zou *et al.*, 1996). When buffalo heifers on rice straw diets were supplemented with urea-MNBs, daily gains were 650 g, compared to 620 g for control animals. Feed cost and concentrate consumption per kilogram of gain were 9.82 and 33.3 percent lower for supplemented buffaloes than those without. Animals showed no signs of poisoning despite block intakes above 1.0 kg/d, indicating that the blocks were safe. Zou *et al.* (1996) selected a formula of MNBs for growing buffaloes that contained molasses, urea, grain by-products, minerals and vitamin premix. Intake of the blocks increased with time, and was 172.4, 330.2 and 374.1 g/day at 30, 60 and 80 days, respectively, from the start of the experiment. Compared to control animals, buffaloes with blocks showed higher weight gain (22.6 percent; 395.4 vs 484.6 g/day) and used 22.5 percent less feed and 22.8 percent less concentrate per kg of gain.

CONCLUDING REMARKS

Ammoniated cereal straws and stovers can be offered to beef cattle, heifers, sheep and goats as sole roughage or as large proportion of the diet. Undoubtedly, supplementation has one of the greatest potentials for improving cereal straw use by ruminants. Animal productive performance can be greatly improved by supplementing with protein sources, concentrate or highly digestible forages, or a combination. In order to obtain satisfactory animal performance, a small amount of protein supplement (below 20 percent of diet DM) is sufficient with ammoniated crop residues, but more protein supplements are needed with untreated straw. The supplementation level with forage depends on the type of forage and basal diet used. A high substitution rate would be possible when higher levels of forage are supplemented. Manufacture and utilization of MNBs as supplements for ruminant animals have increased considerably in China. Much progress has been made and new technologies have been developed since this technique was introduced in the late 1980s. It has been demonstrated that MNBs can be used to improve the productive performance of animals with access to low quality roughage. It was discovered that use of feeding blocks cut methane emissions by half, reducing its contribution to environmental pollution.

Chapter 6

Machinery and equipment for utilization of crop residues as feed

Guo Peiyu
China Agricultural University
Han Lujia
China Agricultural University

TECHNOLOGY FLOW AND EQUIPMENT

The handling of straw for feed on individual farms in China has mostly been done manually, with the aid of little machinery. However, with increased scales of production and reduced labour force as town enterprises develop and attract away workers, it is inevitable that there will be a gradual move towards mechanization of animal husbandry. Of course, the process will a take long time considering the situation in the country. The purpose of this chapter is to introduce machinery and equipment suitable for different levels of mechanization of straw feeding. It will present types, uses and selection principles of machinery and equipment for upgrading and utilizing straw as feed.

The technical flow from straw collection and processing to feeding could take many routes, from simple to complex, depending on the level of upgrading, the nutritive value of the straw, and commercialization of straw products (Figure 6-1).

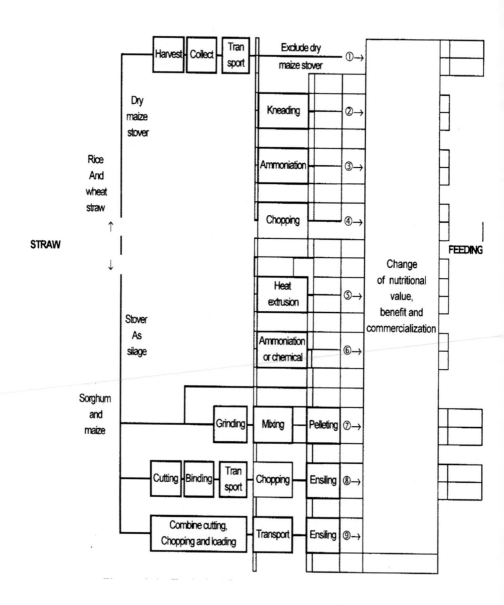

Figure 6-1. Technical flow chart of residue processing

Flows ① and ④ are manual handling systems, some elements of which can be replaced by machines nowadays. Flow ② is the best processing method to increase intake and utilization of an entire crop without further treatment than the kneading into thread-like pieces. This is appropriate for maize stover of high nutrient value. The final process of flows ③ and ⑥ is ammonia treatment. The difference between flows ③ and ⑥ is that ③ is used for whole straw, such as rice and wheat straw, while ⑥ is suitable for maize stover. The final step of flow ⑤ is heat extrusion. Its key part is the heat extrusion equipment. Flow ⑦ shows that, after ammonia and chemical treatment, straw needs to be ground and mixed with nutrients, and finally pelleted or wafered. Straw treated by this method has the advantages of being of high density, easy to store and transport (marketing), reduces waste at feeding and avoids diet selection by the animal.

Both flows ⑧ and ⑨ are suitable for ensiling maize or sorghum stover. In flow ⑧, harvesting, bundling, transporting, chopping and loading into a trench silo are performed separately, and most of them can be done manually, but the chopper or so-called "silage cutter" is absolutely necessary. In flow ⑨, the residues are harvested, chopped and loaded into the wagon using a combine, then transferred to a silo.

The processes used for upgrading of straw for feeding and the machinery options are listed in Table 6-1.

Table 6-1. Machinery selection for various technical processes in upgrading straw

Process	Machine type
Straw collection	Rectangular baler; round baler; stacker; stationary baler.
Loading and transport	Bale loader mounted on wagon or trailer; round bale wagon; stack-mover; wagon; trailer.
Kneading and cutting	Kneading and cutting machine.
Chopping	Cylinder chopper; flywheel chopper.
Heat extrusion	Heat-extrusion equipment.
Ammonia treatment	Ammonia treatment equipment at normal temperature; heated ammonia equipment; ammoniation tank; ammoniation oven.
Grinding	Hammer mill; fixed head mill; claw-type mill; double roller mill.
Pelleting or wafering	Pelleting equipment; wafering equipment.
Silage cutting, chopping and loading	Silage combine and trailer.

COLLECTION, LOADING AND TRANSPORT EQUIPMENT

Collection, loading and transport equipment for long and loose straw
Straw collector

It is used to collect straw into small stacks, or to bring them to a large one. It consists of a collecting platform, left and right handspikes, a frame and a pulley support (Figure 6-2). The collecting platform includes a collecting fork, a side bar and a fence.

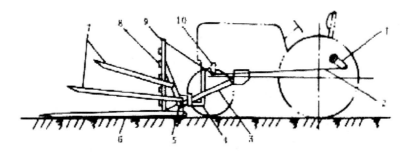

Figure 6-2. Straw collector

KEY: 1. Hydraulic arms; 2. Steel cable; 3. Handspike; 4. Frame; 5. Suspension spring; 6. Collecting fork; 7. Side bar; 8. Fence; 9. Supporting frame; 10. Pulley support.

The machine slides forward, with an angle of 5-7° from the ground, to collect straw with the fork. When the fork is full, hydraulic arms are engaged to lift it about 30 cm high from the ground. Then the tractor moves straw to the stack. After lowering the platform, the tractor is backed to unload the straw. There is no stereotype for this machine. Because of its simple structure, users can construct them themselves.

Stacker

There are many types of stacker, including derrick stackers, fan stackers, conveyor belt stackers, slide stackers and hydraulic stackers. For a hydraulic stacker (Figure 6-3), the operation is the following:

(i)   the collecting platform is lowered;

(ii)   the straw-pushing board (3) is moved back by the hydraulic cylinder (2);

(iii)   the collecting fork is used to gather the straw until it is full;

(iv)   the large arm (6) lifts it;

(v)   a hydraulic cylinder opens cover (1);

(vi)   the hydraulic cylinder (2) moves the straw pushing board (3) forward and pushes the straw out.

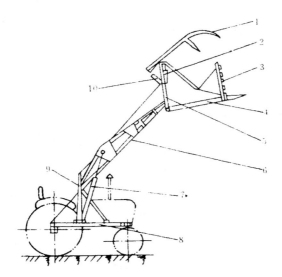

Figure 6-3. Straw stacker

KEY: 1. Cover; 2. Hydraulic piston for pushing straw board; 3. Pushing straw board; 4. Collecting forks; 5. Vertical arms; 6. Large arms; 7. Main hydraulic cylinder; 8. Main frame; 9. Vertical pole; 10. Hydraulic cylinder for cover.

Pick-up-and-press stacker

This consists of a flail-type pick-up chopper, a blower tube with rectangular cross section, a directing cover, a movable top cover, a chamber, a chamber rear door, and a chain conveyor for discharging (Figure 6-4).

The flail type pick-up chopper is used to pick up and chop straw. The airflow, generated by the high-speed rotation of the chopper, blows straw into the chamber through the tube and directing cover. When the chamber is full, the tractor stops moving forward. The top cover is moved down by the compression mechanism to press the straw into the chamber, then the top cover is lifted again. The machine continues to go forward picking up straw again. Generally, a stack can be formed by repeating the above process two or three times. In order to discharge (unload) the stack, the tractor is stopped, the rope is pulled to unlock the chamber's rear door, the hydraulic piston is activated to lift the top cover to its highest position. The chamber's rear door and the top cover open automatically at the same time and the chain conveyor is engaged automatically to move the stack out. When the stack touches the ground, the tractor is driven forward slowly so as to unload the stack on the ground.

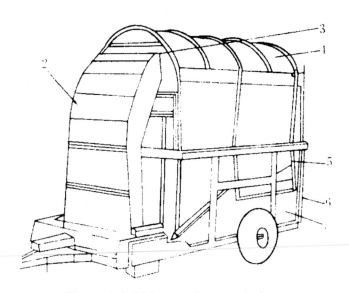

Figure 6-4. Pick-up-and-press stacker

KEY: 1. Flail-type pick-up chopper; 2. Rectangular blower tube; 3. Directing cover; 4. Movable top cover; 5. Compression mechanism; 6. Rear chamber door; 7. Chamber.

The technical parameters of the 9JD-3.6 pickup stacker made in Qiqihaer agricultural and livestock machinery plant are:

- Overall dimensions (cm):   length, 724; width, 398; height, 458.5
- Net weight: 4 200 kg
- Chamber volume: 33 m^3
- Power source: 44.4-73.5 kW tractor
- Working width: 198 cm

- Stack dimensions (cm):   length, 430; width, 260; height, 300
- Stack weight: ca 3 000 kg
- Stack density: 70-110 kg/m³

Stack wagon (stack conveyer)

When the straw stack made by the pick-up-and-press stacker is to be used, it needs to be transported to the feeding site by the stack wagon. The stack wagon (Figure 6-5) is a large platform supported by wheels. On the platform, there are three conveying chains with claws driven by a hydraulic motor fitted at the rear of a pick-up roller and a supporting roller. In operation, the wagon is backed up to the stack. The platform is tilted by the hydraulic cylinder so that the rear roller touches the ground. Then the pickup roller is inserted under the stack. The stack is moved up onto wagon by the combined action of the pickup rollers and reversing of the tractor. When the stack is on the wagon, the platform is returned to the horizontal position and can move off with the stack. After arriving at the feeding site, the platform is tilted again; the chain conveyors are driven in reverse to unload the stack.

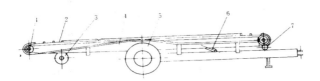

Figure 6-5. Stack wagon

KEY: 1. Pick-up roller; 2. Conveying chains with claws; 3. Supporting roller; 4. Large platform; 5. Road wheels; 6. Hydraulic cylinder; 7. Hydraulic motor.

The technical parameters of the 7DY-3.6 stack wagon made in Qiqihaer Agricultural and Livestock Machinery Plant are:
- Overall dimensions (cm):   length, 705; width, 277; height, 95
- Overall weight: 1 200 kg
- Power source: 20 kW from tractor
- Carrying capacity: 3 600 kg
- Road speed: 25 km/hour

Balers

A baler is a machine used to compress hay or straw into bales for easy transport and storage. A bale is the simplest minimum package for marketing.

Balers are divided into stationary balers and field balers. They are further classified into rectangular balers and round balers according to the bale shape produced. According to density of bale, they could be high (200-350 kg/m³), medium (100-200 kg/m³) or low density (<100 kg/m³) balers.

Rectangular pick-up baler

The 9KJ-1.4A rectangular pick-up baler (Figure 6-6), made by the Inner Mongolia Baochang Livestock Machinery Plant, is used as an example for the general structure and function of rectangular pick-up balers. It makes bales from the straw windrow left by the combine. The machine consists principally of a pick-up reel, a conveying and feeding system, a compressing chamber, a bale density adjuster, a bale length controller, a needle-and-tying mechanism, a crank-linkage mechanism, a power transmission, and hauling system.

It is powered from the power take-off (PTO) of the hauling tractor. The straw windrow is lifted from the ground by a pick-up reel having spring teeth (14) and transferred continuously to a conveying and feeding mechanism (3) as the baler moves forward along the windrow. The conveying and feeding mechanism (3) pushes individual charges of hay into the bale chamber (6) from the side at intervals when the piston (2) is withdrawn. The piston reciprocates under the function of the crank-linkage mechanism to press the material into the bale. When the bale reaches the required length, the needle-and-tying mechanism is engaged automatically to bind the bale, which is then pushed out from the chamber by successive bales and is discharged to the ground.

Rectangular bales can be lifted and loaded either by hand or by a loading machine mounted on the side of a truck or trailer and driven by a ground wheel. The Jilin Baicheng Agricultural and Livestock Machinery Factory also make this kind of baler, model 9JKC-2.7.

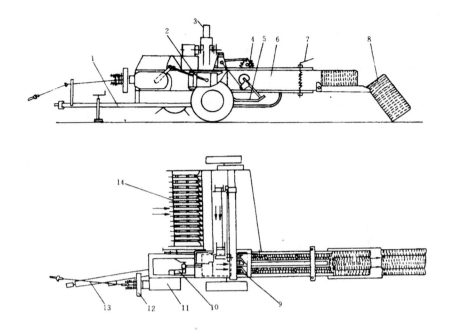

Figure 6-6. Structure and operation of a 9KJ-1.4A baler

KEY: 1. Tow beam; 2. Piston; 3. Conveying and feeding equipment; 4. Bale length controller; 5. Needles; 6. Compression chamber (bale chamber); 7. Bale density adjuster; 8. Bale; 9. Needle-and-tying mechanism; 10. Crank; 11. Main gear box; 12. Flywheel; 13. Universal joint gearing axis; 14. Pick-up reel.

Basic specifications of the 9KJ-1.4A rectangular baler:

- Overall dimension (cm):   length, 480; width, 270; height, 145
- Power source: 22 kW from tractor PTO
- Working speed and output: 5 km/hour; 5 000 - 7 000 kg/hour
- Piston frequency: 70-80 strokes per minute
- Feed rate: 1.5-2.5 kg per cycle
- Nominal pick-up width: 141.4 cm
- Working width: 160 cm
- Bale size (cm):   Length, 60-120; width, 46; height, 36
- Bale weight and density: 15-25 kg; 100-180 kg/m^3
- Baler net weight: 1 480 kg

High density baler

The 92FY-300 high density baler (Figure 6-7) manufactured by the Inner Mongolia Yakeshi Forestry Machinery Plant is taken as an example to describe basic structure and working process. It is a stationary baler equipped with front and rear wheels. It can be hauled to the working site by a tractor. The density of the bale reaches 300 kg/m^3. An electric or diesel motor or the tractor's PTO can supply the power (17 kW). A belt, a chain and a gear by a linkage mechanism drive an eccentric axis that moves the piston back-and-forth. At the same time, the conveying mechanism moves up-and-down to feed the straw into the compression chamber. The bales are fastened with three steel wires (diameter, 2 mm; length, 210 cm).

Basic specifications are:

- Overall baler dimensions (cm):   length, 77; width, 150; height, 254
- Net weight of the baler: 4 tonne.
- Bale size (cm):   length, 50-65; width, 36; height, 46
- Bale weight: 30-35 kg.
- Piston displacement;   62 cm
- Piston frequency: 30 times per minute
- Output: 50-80 bales per hour
- Reference price: ¥ 35 000

Figure 6-7. High density baler

Round baler

The round baler is a new kind of pickup baler. The bales are round, 90-200 cm in diameter. It has the advantages of simple structure and convenience for adjusting and use. The round bales resist the rain, are convenient for feeding and adapted to outside storage. They also save on wire. As a result, they are being increasingly used.

Based on the form of working unit, round balers can be classified into long-belt type, short-belt type, chain type and roller type. They are also classified into inside winding type and outside winding type by their working principle. Long-belt and chain types are inside winding; short-belt and roller types are outside winding.

Figure 6-8 illustrates a belt, inside winding pick-up baler that consists of a pick-up reel, a conveying and feeding mechanism, a wrapping and pressing mechanism, a rear door for unloading, a transmission mechanism and a hydraulic operating mechanism. Its working process is shown in Figure 6-9. The windrow is lifted by a pickup reel (4) and rolled up to double smooth rollers (3) where it is pressed into a flat layer, then conveyed to the baler chamber. With the upper belt the straw moves upward by friction to a certain height, then rolls down to the lower belt by gravity to form the core of the bale, which continually rolls, increasing the diameter. When the bale reaches the desired size it is discharged from the lower belt. The springs fixed in the swing arms in the two sides of the bale chamber maintain the pressure of the belt on the bale's surface. The pressure increases with bale size, resulting in low density on the inside of the bale but high density on the outside. Inside wrapping means that the volume of the wrapping and pressing chamber enlarges during pressing to keep a constant pressure on the bale. The bales formed by inside wrapping have much higher density than by outside wrapping and keep their shape for longer during storage. However, the structure of an inside wrapping baler is more complicated. When the bale reaches the desired size, an indicator alerts the driver to engage the hydraulic distributor in order to activate the binding mechanism. The twine is passed by the tube and fed with straw to the chamber. The twine is wrapped around the circumference of the bale, then cut by a blade. The rear door is lifted hydraulically. The bale is then discharged to the ground.

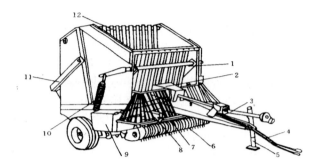

Figure 6-8. Inside wrapping pick-up round baler

KEY: 1. Swing arms; 2. Gear box; 3. Gearing shaft; 4. Hydraulic power supply tube; 5. Support frame; 6. Pick-up reel; 7. Tube for the twine; 8.Twine cutter; 9. Twine box; 10. Tension spring; 11. Rear discharge door; 12. Belt of wrapping and pressing chamber.

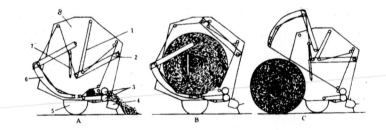

Figure 6-9. Operating principle of the wrapping and pressing mechanism

STAGES: A. Forming of the core of the bale. B. Making the bale. C. Discharging the bale

KEY: 1. Upper belt; 2. Swing arms; 3. Smooth rollers; 4. Pick-up reel; 5. Road wheels; 6. Rear door for discharging; 7. Hydraulic cylinder; 8. Side walls.

The round baler manufactured by the Jilin Baicheng Agricultural and Livestock Machinery Plant belongs to this type. Its specifications are:

- Overall dimensions (cm):   length, 485; width, 245, height, 243
- Net weight: 1 900 kg
- Power source: 40.4 kW from tractor hydraulic system
- Working speed and output: 5 km/hour; 8-12 bale/hour

- Bale weight: 450-500 kg
- Bale diameter and width: 180 cm; 150 cm
- Width of pick-up: 140 cm

Round bales must be loaded, transported and unloaded by machine due to their heavy weight. The 7KY-4 round bale transporting wagon made in China is hydraulically driven and equipped with an automatic pickup mechanism. It can pickup and load round bales with flexibility and accuracy. Four bales can be transported simultaneously.

Harvesting machine for maize silage

Several new cultivars of maize have been popularized in large areas of China, and some of these cultivars have a green stalk at harvest, so they are fit for ensiling. Stover can be harvested, chopped and loaded by a long-stalk cutting platform fitted to a silage harvester (also called a silage combine), and then put into the silo. The 9SQ-10 cylinder-type forage harvester made by the Chifeng Livestock Machinery Plant belongs to this type. When the machine is equipped with a long-stalk cutting platform, its parameters are as follows:

- Dimensions (cm): length, 620; width, 310; height, 288.6
- Weight: 1 180 kg;
- Power supply: 40.4-58.8 kW from tractor
- Cylindrical chopping device:
    cylinder rotation speed: 1 120 rpm;
    cutting blades: 6
    harvesting rows: 2
    distance between rows: 60 or 70 cm
    stalk cutter: double disc-type

The Beijing Combine Factory has designed a self-propelled maize harvester (model 4YZ-4) that accomplishes picking, husking, ear collecting, stover and leaf chopping, and returning to the ground or throwing into a trailer as a single-pass operation. It is well suited to harvest maize before sowing wheat. It harvests four 70-cm rows with an efficiency of 1-2.5 ha/hour. The engine power is 110.25 kW, and its weight is 9 tonne. The reference price is ¥ 150 000.

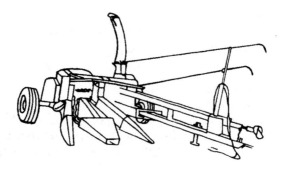

Figure 6-10. Cylinder-type silage harvester with thrower

CROP RESIDUE PROCESSING MACHINES

Choppers

The chopper is mainly used for stalk forage, such as rice straw, wheat straw, maize stover and maize for ensiling. Straw choppers can be classified by size into small, medium and large. The small-size chopper is mainly adapted for chopping dry straw or silage on small-scale farms. The large chopper – also called a silage chopper – is mainly used for silage on cattle farms. The medium chopper is normally suited to cutting dry straw and silage, so it is called a straw-silage chopper.

Choppers can be divided into cylinder or flywheel types, according to the mode of cutting. Large- and medium-size choppers are generally flywheel types, to facilitate throwing silage, but the majority of small choppers are cylinder type. Large and medium choppers are usually equipped with road wheels for easy movement, while small-size choppers are normally stationary.

Cylinder choppers

There are many types of cylinder chopper. The 93ZT-100 chopper (Figure 6-11), made by Wulanhaote Livestock Machinery Factory in Inner Mongolia, is taken as an example to describe the structure of a chopper.

The machine consists primarily of mechanisms for feeding, chopping, and throwing, with a transmission, a clutch and a frame. The principles of operation are illustrated in Figure 6-12.

The main parts of the feed mechanism are a chain conveyor, pressing rollers, and upper and lower feed rollers. For the upper feed roller, springs are used for pressure, with a cross-groove shaft coupled with a compact structure for driving. The chopping and throwing mechanism is in one unit, which consists of a main shaft, a blade rotor, rotating blades, a throwing vane and stationary blades. Gear teeth are 13, 22, 65 or 56. By changing the gear used, the speed can be adjusted to obtain various cutting lengths.

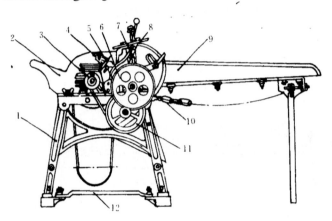

Figure 6-11. 93ZT-1000 straw chopper

KEY: 1. Frame; 2. Throwing cover; 3. Small single-groove sheave; 4. Blades disk; 5. Movable blade; 6.Changeable gear; 7. Wheel-tension clutch; 8. Suspension bracket; 9. Feeding groove; 0. Chain; 11. Large single-groove sheave; 12. Supporting plate for motor.

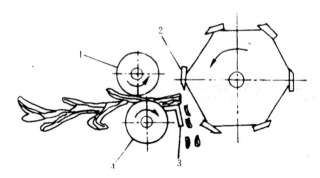

Figure 6-12. Chopping action of cylinder-type straw chopper

KEY: 1. Upper feed roller; 2. Cylinder blade. 3. Stationary bottom blade; 4. Lower feed roller.

Flywheel choppers

Flywheel chopper operation is illustrated in Figure 6-13, showing a feed chain, upper and lower feed rollers, a stationary lower blade, a cutter and a throwing fan. The straw is fed via the feed chain into the feed rollers, pressed and moved forward by them, then cut into pieces by the combination of upper and lower blades, and it is finally blown by the fan to the storage site or silo.

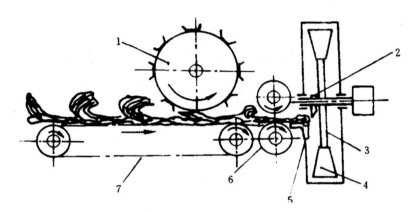

Figure 6-13. Chopping action of the disk chopper

KEY: 1. Feed roller; 2. Blade; 3. Disk; 4. Blower fan; 5. Stationary bottom blade;
6. Feed roller; 7. Feed chain

Figure 6-14 shows the outline of a 93ZP-1000 straw chopper produced by the Liaoning Fengcheng Donsfeng Machinery Factory. Its output is 1 000 kg/hour, the length of chopped pieces are 15 mm or 35 mm and the rotary speed of the main shaft is 8 000 rpm. It has 2 movable blades, a power supply of 3 kW from an integral motor, weighs 110 kg, and its overall dimensions are 95 cm long, 98 cm wide and 140 cm high.

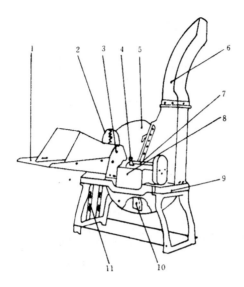

Figure 6-14. Structure of a 93ZP-1000 type chopper

KEY: 1. Feed channel; 2. Bow shape frame; 3. Supporting frame for rollers; 4. Handle for changing position; 5. Cover; 6. Outlet for straw; 7. Connecting shaft; 8. Gearbox; 9. Chassis; 10. Movable blade; 11. Motor frame.

Some types of straw choppers, their technical parameters and their manufacturers in China are shown in Table 6-2.

Grinders
Grinding methods and grinder types
There are four main grinding methods: impacting, grinding, crushing and sawing (see Figure 6-15). Impacting is suitable for hard and brittle raw materials, such as maize feed; sawing is better for large and fragile feed; and crushing and grinding are used for tough feed.

Table 6-2. Some chopper types, their technical parameters and manufacturers in China

Model	Type & Speed (rpm)	Cutting length (mm)	Power (kW) & Capacity (kg/hour)	Weight (kg) & Size (l◊w◊h; cm)	Price (¥)	Maker
93ZP-400 Straw chopper (*Feima*)	Flywheel 900	15, 35	0.75 / 400	33 / 70◊55◊50	730	(1)
93ZP-1000 Straw chopper (*Feima*)	Flywheel 800	15, 35	3.0 / 1 000	110 / 95◊98◊140	1 190	(1)
93ZP-1600 Straw chopper (*Feima*)	Flywheel 800	15, 35	4.0 / 1 600	115 / n.a.	1 235	(1)
93ZQ-400 Straw and veg. chopper (*Feima*)	Flywheel 900	5, 7, 15, 35	0.75 / 400	35 / 70◊55◊50	757	(1)
9QF-45 Silage chopper (*Feima*)	Flywheel 1000	16	7.5-11 / 1 500	200 / 152◊99◊80	2 927	(1)
9ZP-4.0 Straw chopper	Flywheel 700	15, 22, 35, 50	13.0 / 4 000	515 / 253◊248◊1773	6 300	(2)
PCC-60 Silage chopper	Flywheel 450	6-106	10.0 / 9 000	1000 / 284◊177◊205	6 300	(2)
9ZP-1.6 Straw and veg. chopper (*Fenglei*)	Flywheel	15, 20, 35	3.0 Grass 2 000 Straw 3 000	n.a. n.a.		(3)
9DQ-100 Silage chopper (*Wuye*)	Flywheel 600	9, 20, 28, 60	4.0 Straw 2 500 700-6 500	335 / 150◊55◊126	1 680	(4)
93ZT-1000 Straw chopper (*Xing'anling*)		13, 26	3.0 / 1 000	190 / 175◊60◊110	1 188	(5)
9Z-4 Straw chopper	Cylinder 1200	15-20	5.5 Grass 6 000 Straw 1 500	280 / n.a.	4 100	(6)
9Z-8 Straw chopper (*Ximmu*)	Flywheel 600	15, 14	n.a. Grass 12 000 Straw 3 000			(6)
9ZCA-1.0 Straw chopper	Cylinder 775	13, 26	3.0 / 1 000	195 / 175◊60◊110	800	(7)
9ZC-6 Straw chopper	Cylinder 650	6, 13, 25	10.0 Silage 6 000	1000 / 250◊180◊195	5 700	(8)
93ZP-2500 Straw chopper (*Ximmu*)	Flywheel 850	8-25	7.5 / 2 500	320 / 238◊134◊173		(9)

NOTE: n.a. = information not supplied.

KEY TO MANUFACTURERS: (1) Liaoning Fengcheng Dongfeng Machinery Plant. (2) Beijing Linhai Agricultural and Livestock Machinery Plant. (3) Beijing Yanjing Livestock Machinery Co. (4) Shijiazhuang Agricultural and Livestock Machinery Plant. (5) Inner Mongolia Wulanhote Livestock Machinery Plant. (6) Shandong Feicheng Chopper Plant. (7) Henan Fugou Scientific Instrument Plant (MOA). (8) Shanxi Xi'an Livestock and Milk Machinery Plant. (9) Xinjiang Livestock Machinery Plant.

Many mills combine different methods. Those commonly found are hammer, fixed head, claw and roller mills. The hammer mill is well suited for straw feed. The roller mill uses a pair of opposed toothed rollers that rotate simultaneously in opposite directions and at different speeds to grind the feed. Roller mills are mainly used for grinding oil cakes. The principles of operation are illustrated in Figure 6-15 (5).

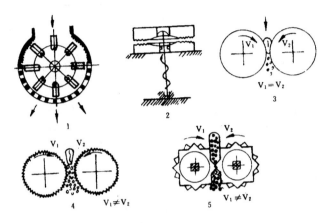

Figure 6-15. Grinding methods for feed

KEY: 1. Impacting; 2. Grinding; 3. Pressing; 4, 5. Sawing.

Hammer mills

Hammer mills grind material by the impact of a high-speed rotary hammer. Hammer mills are either tangential-feed or axial-feed types, according to their structure.

Figure 6-16 shows the structure of the 9FQ-50 tangential-feed mill made by the Hongxing Machinery Factory in Jiangxi Province. The mill comprises a feeding part, a grinding chamber and a collector. The feeding part comprises a feed hopper and a feed control flap. The grinding chamber consists of a rotary disk, a hammer, a serrated plate and a screen. The major parts of the collector include a fan, a feed conveying tube and a collection hopper.

Fed from the feed hopper in a tangential direction, the material is impacted and driven to the grinding chamber by the rotating hammers with high speed. The material in the grinding chamber is firstly hit and ground to some extent by hammers, and then thrown at high speed at the serrated plate and the peripheral screen fixed inside the chamber to be further ground through impact with the serrated plate and friction with the screen.

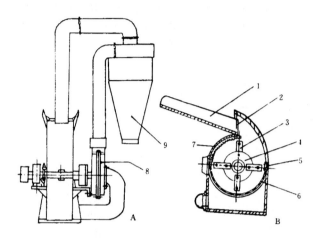

Figure 6-16. Tangential-feed grinder

KEY: 1. Feed hopper; 2. Feed control; 3. Swinging hammer; 4. Rotary disk; 5. Small serrated plate; 6. Peripheral screen; 7. Large serrated plate; 8. Fan; 9. Feed gathering (collection) hopper.

The process then repeats until the particles pass through the screen and are discharged from the grinding chamber. The process inside the grinding chamber includes the functions of impacting, shearing and kneading, which improves the efficiency of grinding. The feed product is sucked from the discharging door to the conveying tube by a fan, then enters the collection hopper, and is finally discharged from the collection hopper after the meal settles out from the air stream.

The axial-feed mill (Figure 6-17) differs from the tangential-feed mill in both the direction of feeding and in primary cutting action. Straw fed from the axial-feed hopper is firstly chopped into small pieces by the primary cutting mechanism fixed in front of the grinding chamber, and these pieces then fall into the grinding chamber. Thus the load on the grinding chamber is reduced; and the feeding capability and efficiency of processing improved. The axial-feed mill is especially suited to grinding straw with high moisture content.

The advantages of the hammer mill are high productivity, wide application and fine particle output. It can be used to mill maize, concentrate feed, green grass and various straws with high moisture and fibre content, so it is also called a "grass powder miller." However, energy consumption is high.

The fixed-head mill differs from the hammer mill in that its blade is fixed to the rotary disk rather than connected to it by a pin, so it has much higher grinding capacity.

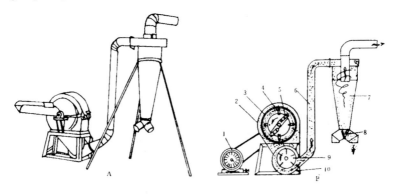

Figure 6-17. Axial-feed mill. A. Outline; B. Operation.

KEY: 1. Motor; 2. Housing; 3. Ring screen; 4. Hammer; 5. Primary cutter; 6. Conveying tube; 7. Feed collection (gathering) hopper; 8. Discharging door and tube; 9. Fan; 10. Frame.

Claw mills

Claw mills hit and grind material with claws fixed in a rotating disc, and are suitable for concentrate grinding because of compact structure, small volume and light weight.

Figure 6-18 illustrates the structure of a claw mill with its feeding, grinding and discharging parts. The feeding includes a feed hopper, a feed control door and a feed tube. The grinding part consists of a rotary serrated disk, a stationary serrated disk and a ring screen. Claws are fixed on the rotary and the stationary disks alternatively. The discharging part is a tube situated in the bottom of the machine.

After flowing into the grinding chamber from the feed hopper via the feeding door, the material is impacted, sheared, kneaded and gradually rubbed by claws into powder. At the same time, the airflow formed by high-speed rotation of the rotary serrated disk blows the powder out through the ring screen.

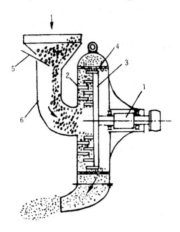

Figure 6-18. Claw mill

KEY: 1. Main shaft; 2. Stationary serrated disk; 3. Rotary serrated disk; 4. Ring screen; 5. Door to control material input rate; 6. Feed tube.

Factors influencing the effects of grinding

(i) **Type of material to be ground**. The grinding output with the same energy consumption differs according to raw material. Output with cereal feed is higher than with roughage. With a screen hole diameter of 1.2 mm and a moisture content below 15 percent, the output in kg/kW is 45-60 for maize and sorghum; 17-22 for chaff; 12-16 for sweet potato vines; 8-12 for maize stover; 7-12 for sorghum stover; 6-10 for legume straw; and 3-4 for maize cobs (2 mm screen hole diameter).

(ii) **Moisture content**. The higher the moisture content, the lower the output and the poorer the energy efficiency. Generally, moisture content should not be higher than 15 percent.

(iii) **Rotary speed of main shaft**. Each type of mill has a range of rotary speeds for the main shaft to obtain high output and low energy consumption for each feed. If the rotary speed is too low, the grinding capacity is decreased and feed discharge is hampered, so productivity is also reduced. In contrast, if the rotary speed is too high, idle energy consumption is increased, as well as wear, tear and vibration, and the total energy consumed is higher. The line speed for hammer mills made in China in recent years is about 70 –90 m/sec.

(iv) **Feed rate**. If the feed rate is too high, ground feed can not be discharged from the grinding chamber at the same rate, which results in clogging, which affects capacity. In contrast, if the feeding rate is too low, the milling capacity is not fully used and efficiency decreases.

The main mill types made in China are listed in Table 6-3.

Kneading machines

The kneading machine is a new kind of straw processing technique developed in China, combining chopping with grinding. The machine processes residues, especially maize stover, into thin thread segments of 8-19 cm, completely destroying its node structure. Palatability is greatly improved, and the intake of the entire crop is also increased to 95 percent from the original 50 percent. The structure of the kneading machine is shown in Figure 6-19. In operation, the rotor, diameter 40 cm, rotates at a high-speed (2 856 rpm) driving 16 hammers arranged in 4 groups, which impact the straw fed continually. A tilted serrated plate, whose teeth are arranged helically and with changeable height, and 6 stationary blades are fixed to the concave plate of the machine, in order to keep the impacted straw moving in axially with the help of a fan. Taking the 9RC-40 kneading machine, made by the Beijing Linhai Agricultural and Livestock Machinery Plant, as an example: the power supply is 7.5 -13 kW (the machine can also be driven by 8.82 -11.0 kW from a four-wheel drive tractor) and the output of model I is up to 1 000 kg/hour, with 2 000 kg/hour from model II.

The kneading machine can increase straw utilization considerably simply by physical processing and it is well suited for maize stover, which already has high nutrient value. Energy consumption is high, 1 to 2 times that of a normal chopping machine of the same output, because the final particles are finer. Because straw can also be softened during ensilage or ammoniation, this chopper can meet animals' requirements when they do not directly eat straw.

The main types and technical parameters of the kneading machines made in China are shown in Table 6-4.

Table 6-3. Characteristics of some grinders produced in China

Model and Type*	Speed Rotor Δ (mm) Screen (mm)	Output – Maize – Straw (kg/kWh)	Capacity – Maize – Straw (kg/hour)	Power (kW)	Weight (kg) Size (l◊w◊h; cm)	Price (¥)	Maker
9FQ-40B Feed mill (*Fenglei*) [H]	3800 rpm 400; –	95 22	800 160	7.5	150 83◊79◊90	790	(1)
9QF-50B Feed mill (*Fenglei*) [H]	3250 rpm 500; –	95 20	1300 260	13.0	240 107◊106◊99	1 600	(1)
6FC-308A Feed mill [Fixed head]	3800 rpm 308; –	n.a. –	600 –	5.5	120 75◊56◊120	760	(2)
9FQ40-20 Feed mill [H]	n.a.	n.a. –	1000 –	7.5-11	170 90◊89◊81	850	(2)
9F-45A High efficiency feed mill (*Fengshou*) [H]	3600 rpm 450; 1.2	90 30	900 300	10.0	130 88◊87◊105	865	(3)
9F-36 Feed mill (*Fengshou*)	4 500 rpm 360; 2	n.a.	1000 280	7.5	85 75◊99◊114	780	(3)
9FQ40-20 Straw Mill (*Fengshou*) [H]	3 770 rpm n.a.	n.a.	1100 –	7.5-11	170 99◊89◊81	850	(3)
9FQ-40 Feed mill [H]	– 400; 2.0	95 25	900 200	7.5-11	200 90◊57◊81	1 297	(4)
9F-45A Feed mill [H]	3 600 rpm –; 2	n.a.	1090 –	11	n.a.	n.a.	(5)
9FS-45A Feed mill [C]	3200 rpm –; 2	n.a.	780 –	11	n.a.	n.a.	(5)
93FC-50 Straw Mill (*Hongxing*) [H]	3437 rpm 500; 3	134 78	1519 706	15	184◊105◊95	8 000	(6)
9FQ40-20 Feed mill (*Hongxing*) [H]	3730 rpm 400; 2	130 22	1000 165	7.6	180 n.a.	1 200	(6)
9FQ-50 Feed mill (*Hongxing*) [H]	3440 rpm 500; 1.2	69 13.7	884 175	13	488 156◊61◊210	1 800	(6)
9F-37-1 Feed mill (*Lingfeng*) [H]	4000 rpm 370; 1	n.a.	250 50	7.5	125 69◊70◊68	700	(7)
9F-500 Feed mill (*Dongyue*) [H]	3250 rpm 500; 3.5	> 125 > 20	850 400	11	200 154◊97◊154	1 320	(8)
9F-400 Feed mill (*Dongyue*) [H]	3000 rpm 400; 3.5	> 142 > 25	600 250	7.5	150 149◊99◊146	1 100	(8)
93Fc-650 Straw Mill (*Xinmu*) [H]	2500 rpm 650; 4	107 46.8	800 560	11	n.a. 2157◊1274◊1505	3 200	(9)

NOTES: * Types are [H] = hammer; [C] = claw. n.a. = information not provided.
KEY TO MANUFACTURERS: (1) Beijing tonnexian Grinder Plant. (2) Shanxi Huguan Farm Machinery Plant. (3) Inner Mongolia Ningchen General Machinery Plant. (4) Liaoning Fengchen Machinery Plant. (5) Helongjiang Anqing Farm and Livestock Plant. (6) Jiangxi State Running Hongxing Machinery Plant. (7) Gangxi Hoxian Agricultural Machinery Plant. (8) Shandong Taishan Farm and Livestock Machinery Plant. (9) Xinjiang Livestock Machinery Plant

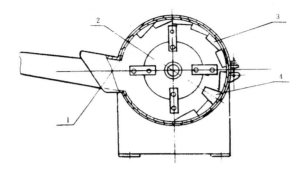

Figure 6-19. Illustration of kneading machine structure

KEY: 1. Smooth plate; 2. Hammer rotor; 3. Unequal height teeth; 4. Stationary blade.

Table 6 -4. Characteristics of some kneading machines in China

Model and type*	Rotor ⌀ (mm) Speed (rpm)	Power (kW) Capacity (kg/hour)	kg/kWh	Weight (kg) Size (l×w×h; cm)	Price (·)	Maker
93RC-40 Straw Kneading Machine [H]	400 2500	7.5 - 10 1000	100	120 13712669	1 640	(1)
93RC-40 Straw Kneading Machine [H]	400 2610	7.5 - 13 2000	n.a.	130 15366127	2 500	(2)
K-67-50 Straw Kneading Machine [H&B]	500 n.a.	n.a.	n.a.	n.a. n.a.	2 000	(3)
9RS-1.5 Straw Kneading Machine [H&B]	n.a. 1400	17 - 22 1500	n.a.	n.a. 16050122	2 800	(4)
9RS-0.7 Straw Kneading Machine [H&B]	n.a. 2000	5.5 - 10 700	n.a.	n.a. 1323783	1 800	(4)
9RSL-50 Multi-function feed Kneading Machine [H&B]	Chopping 900 Tearing 2000 n.a.	7.5 5000	n.a.	195 21554150	1 500	(5)
9RC-40 Straw Kneading Machine [H]	n.a. n.a.	7.5 1000	n.a.	160 n.a.	n.a.	(6)
9FRQ-40B Straw Kneading Machine [D]	n.a. n.a.	n.a.	n.a.	n.a. n.a.	750	(7)
93F-45 Straw Kneading Machine [H]	450 2500	4 200	50	600 18080105	3 200	(8)

NOTES: * machine types are [D] = disc; [H] = hammer; [H&B] = hammer and blade.
      n.a. = information not supplied
KEY TO MANUFACTURERS: (1) Liaoning Fengchen Machinery Plant. (2) Beijing Linhai Farm and Livestock Machinery Plant.
      (3) Helongjiang Achen Huajianuy Metal Structure Plant. (4) Inner Mongolia Chifeng General Livestock Plant.
      (5) Helongjiang Anda Livestock Machinery Plant. (6) Helongjiang Achen Mechanical and Electrical Equipment Plant.
      (7) Jilin Jutai Farm Tool Plant (8) Shanxi Xi an Livestock and Milk Equipment Plant.

Kneading and cutting machines

Kneading and cutting machine models 9LRZ-80 (Figure 6-20) and 9RZ-60 (Figure 6-21) were designed by the Non-conventional Feed Institute, China Agricultural University. They passed appraisal by MOA in 1998. The appraisal said that the machines were an innovation in China, with world-leading performance.

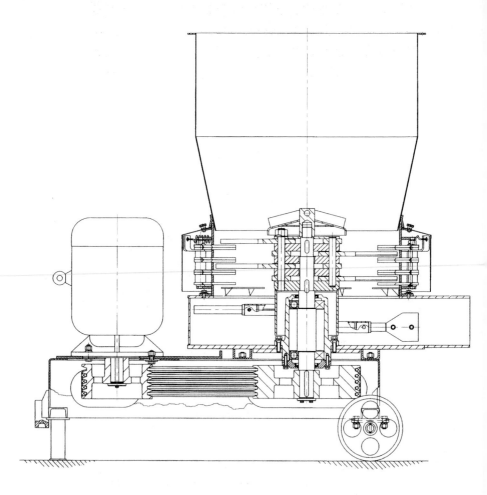

Figure 6-20. Type 9LRZ-80 kneading machine

Kneading and cutting machines combine cutting, kneading and mixing in one operation. Maize stover, wheat and rice straw, bean vine and tuber vine can be processed to thread-like soft material.

The future developments of the series include the replacement of the cutting blades in the chopper by running blades; and the incorporation of a hammer in the kneading machine and of a mixing rotor in the mixer. There are now 16 running blades and 6 sets of fixed blades. Changing the number of running blades and fixed blades will alter the cutting length and softness. The material will be thrown to the inner region of the cylinder, and will be chopped, cut and kneaded to thread-like form. When tubers and concentrate are fed into the machine together, material will be cut and mixed.

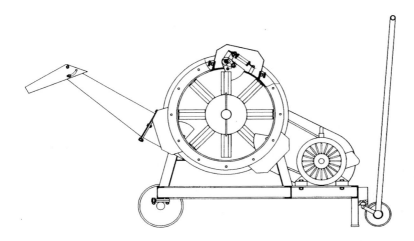

Figure 6-21. Type 9RZ-60 kneading machine

The new series has the following advantages:
• The new axle structure increases the feeding capacity.
• In the working cylinder, the running and the fixed blades will cut and knead at same time, so that energy can obviously be reduced.
• By simply changing blade numbers, different lengths and softness can be obtained. It is suitable for green and dry materials, and especially for wet and tough material (such as palm nut shell, reeds, and chaste tree twigs).

- It is suitable for maize stover silage. The processed material can be compacted easily. Without nodes remaining, the whole stalk can be eaten by the animal.

    The 9LRZ-80 is appropriate for large farms. It requires a power source of 22-30 kW, and has a capacity of 6-8 t/hour, and an output of 0.39 tonne/kWh. Its node breaking efficiency is 99 percent.

    The 9RZ-60 kneading and cutting machine can be equipped with a 15 kW electrical motor. The 9RZC-60 has an 18 hp diesel engine. Both have an output of 3-4 t/hour, and are suitable for medium-sized farms.

Table 6-5. Specifications of kneading and cutting machines

	9LRZ-80	9RZ-60
Power (kW)	22	11-15
Productivity (t/hour)		
With 14-40% moisture	3 – 5	2 – 3
With 40-70% moisture	6 – 8	3 – 4
Grade of processed material		
< 50 mm	ca 78%	
50 - 100 mm	ca 20%	
> 100mm	ca 2 %	
Node breaking efficiency	> 99 %	

Compared to a chopper, the 9LRZ-80 can save 2 160 kWh and 1 080 work-days for processing 6 000 tonne of green stalks. Total savings are about ¥ 3 000.

Pelleting equipment

After being ground into meal, having had concentrates and other nutrient elements added, straw makes a complete feed, and can be pressed by a pelleting machine. The pelleted feed, containing all nutrients, increases palatability and intake, and at the same time decreases feed waste and reduces feeding time. However, the cost of equipment for pellet processing is high. The machine consists of a pelleting device, a steam generator, an oil and molasses doser, a cooling device, a separator and a sieve.

    There are two types of pelleters: disk die and ring die pelleters.

Disk die pelleter

Several disk die pelleters have been made in China. Figure 6-22 shows a disk die pelleter, comprising a screw conveyor, a gear-box, a stirrer and a pelleting device. The screw conveyor, whose rotary speed is adjustable, is mainly used to control the charging rate. The stirrer situated under the conveyor stirs the material, admitting steam through a side hole to heat and cook the material while it is transferred to the pelleting device. Inside the die there are 2 to 4 press rollers and a disk with many holes (shown in Figure 6-23). In operation, the disk rotates at a speed of 210 rpm. After falling onto the disk die, the cooked meal is distributed evenly by a spade and forced through the round holes of the die by the press. The cylindrical pellets from the die are then cut into pieces 10-20 mm long by a blade under the disk. Disk presses can be classified into three types: movable die, movable roller and movable die and roller types. Hole diameter in the die can be 4, 6 or 8 mm. The diameter of the roller ranges from 160 to 180 mm.

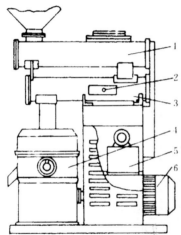

Figure 6-22. Pelleter with disk die

KEY: 1. Screw conveyor; 2. Steam inlet; 3. Stirrer; 4. Press; 5. Wormwheel box; 6. Motor.

Figure 6-23. Operation of the disk die.

Ring die pelleter

The ring die press has been widely used in engineering. Figure 6-24 is an illustration of its operation. The main parts are a screw conveyor, a stirrer, a pelleting device and a drive mechanism. The screw conveyor, whose rotary speed can normally be changed gradually in the range of 0-150 rpm, is used to control the loading rate. A side opening to the stirring chamber allows steam to be injected. In the stirring compartment, the meal is mixed with over-saturated high-pressure steam. Sometimes oil, molasses and other additives are added during mixing. When ideal conditions can not be met, water can be used instead of steam, but in this case mixing is poor, output is decreased, and energy consumption and friction are increased.

The mixed meal goes into the pelleting device, which consists of a ring die and pressing rollers. In operation, the ring die rotates, making the rollers turn and press the material through the cylindrical holes of the ring die. The cylindrical pellets rotate with the ring die, and are cut by a blade. The larger the hole diameter, the higher the output of the machine and the lower the energy consumption. Hole diameter is determined by animal requirements.

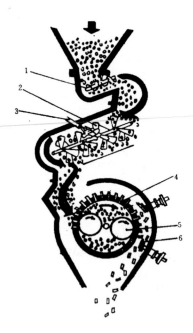

Figure 6-24. Operation of a pelleter with ring die

KEY: 1. Screw conveyor; 2. Stirrer; 3. Steam or air inlet; 4. Ring die; 5. Rollers; 6. Cutter.

Wafering machinery for roughage

Wafers are about ten times the size of pellets. The wafering machine made by the Guangdong Huada Machinery Factory can make rectangular wafers 25 ¥ 25 mm or 30 ¥ 30 mm, and also cylindrical wafers of 8-30 mm in diameter. The density varies from 0.6 to 1.0 g/cm^3, and the bulk weight from 0.4 to 0.6 tonne/m^3. The output is 600-1 000 kg/hour. Five operators are needed.

The 93KWH-40 waferer and the 93KWH complete wafering set have been developed by the Jiangxi Hongxing Machinery Plant. The rotary speed of the main press shaft is 167 rpm, the output is 300-600 kg/h, and the power needed 37 kW. The whole system's energy needs are 62.5 kW.

After milling and addition of concentrates, chemical additives and other minerals, the straw is wafered to increase nutrient value, intake and digestibility. The wafered feed is not only easy to transport, to store and to feed, but also very convenient for marketing due to its high density.

The wafering process is shown in a flow chart (Figure 6-25). After size reduction (chopping, grinding) to a specified size, controlled by the screen holes, roughage such as rice straw, wheat straw, maize stover, bulrush and sunflower stem is transported by forced air to the cyclone (2) and then to the buffering bin (3). The material from the bin (3) is conveyed via a double-screw conveyor (4) and a rationing conveyor (5) to the mixer (8), where chemical additives and concentrates are added separately at prescribed rates from hoppers (6 and 7). At the same time, water and steam are also added to the mixer. The uniformly mixed material falls to the wafering machine (11) to be made into cubes. The cubes are transferred to a horizontal cooler (13), and then drop to the packing machine.

STRAW TREATMENT EQUIPMENT

Ammoniation equipment for ambient conditions

The ammoniation reaction occurs at temperatures above 0°C. Reaction speed increases with temperature. There are many methods for ammoniation under normal temperature, such as stack ammoniation and use of an ammonia silo. Straw ammoniation can be carried out using various sealable containers.

The sources of ammonia for straw treatment are anhydrous ammonia, aqueous ammonia, ammonium bicarbonate and urea. When using aqueous ammonia, ammonium bicarbonate or urea, water should be added at a prescribed rate. Straw uniformly mixed with the ammonia source is sealed in the container for the ammoniation. Anhydrous ammonia is kept as a liquid under high pressure and therefore pressure containers are required to transport and store it. A minimum set of equipment, including perforated metal pipe (ammonia injection spear), volume meter, ammonia pressure meter and some safety equipment, are required for ammonia injection. Because anhydrous ammonia is a potentially dangerous and toxic material, stringent safety measures need to be taken.

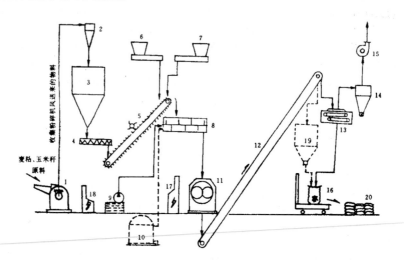

Figure 6-25. Flow chart of 93KCT-1000 complete roughage wafering set operation

KEY: 1. Grinder; 2. Cyclone; 3. Buffering bin; 4. Double-screw conveyor; 5. Rationing conveyor; 6. Chemical additive dosing mechanism; 7. Concentrate adding mechanism; 8. Mixer; 9. Water adding mechanism; 10. Heat source for cooking; 11. Waferer for coarse silage; 12. Tilt conveyor; 13. Horizontal cooler; 14. Cyclone; 15. Fan; 16. Packing machine; 17. Electronic control console; 18. Grinder control console; 19. Final product bin; 20. Product.

Heating equipment for ammoniation

To the north of the Yellow River, the temperature is usually below 0°C in winter, and thus the ammoniation reaction can not happen. In order to deal with this problem, some new ways for ammoniation were developed in these areas.

Heated ammoniation-bunker method

The traditional method for heating material using the smoke channels of a stove – a procedure widely used in rural areas to cultivate sweet potato seedlings in early spring – is used for straw ammoniation. It is called the heated ammoniation-bunker method. The structure of the bunker is shown in Figure 6-26. The operating steps are as follows: a bunker is constructed with brick and concrete, half underground. A stove is built at one end of the bunker, under which there are two smoke channels connected to a chimney at the other end of the stove. Firstly, the straw, mixed with the urea or ammonium bicarbonate solution at recommended doses, is placed into the bunker and sealed. Next, the straw inside the stove is ignited to heat the treated straw during half a day at a temperature of 30°C. The amount of straw burnt is equivalent to 5-10 percent. After a week, the treated straw can be fed. Longer heating times or higher temperature can shorten ammoniation time.

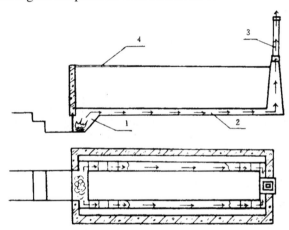

Figure 6-26. Ammoniation bunker for heating

KEY: 1. Stove; 2. Heat channel; 3.Chimney; 4. Plastic sheet

Ammoniation in tobacco curing houses

Tobacco curing houses are usually empty in winter. The straw is placed into the tobacco house, a urea or ammonium bicarbonate solution added, the straw well sealed, and then heated by burning coal. The house is kept at 40-50°C for 3-4 days for the ammoniation to be completed. This is a practical method in tobacco-growing areas.

Ammoniation in ovens

The ammoniation oven has proved to be an efficient item of equipment for livestock farms where straw ammoniation needs to be industrialized and delivered regularly according to a plan. Figure 6-27 outlines an oven with a straw trailer that can be pulled in and out. The source of ammonia can be anhydrous ammonia or ammonium bicarbonate. In Figure 6-27, anhydrous ammonia is used. Of course, anhydrous ammonia needs to be transported and stored in pressure containers. Urea is not suitable for oven ammoniation, with its temperature as high as 90°C, because the ureases required to break down urea are destroyed at these temperatures. There are three heating options: electricity, steam or coal. The oven may be a metal box or of brick construction. The parameters for a 30 m³ metal box-oven heated by electricity are listed in Table 6-5.

Figure 6-27. Oven for ammonia treatment of straw

KEY: 1. Oven; 2. Door; 3. Straw trolley; 4. Track; 5. Straw baler; 6. Ammonia bottle;
7. Perforated metal pipe for ammonia injection (ammonia spear).

When an electric element is used to heat the oven, the temperature and heating time can be automatically controlled using a thermostat and timer. This oven has the advantages of simple operation, time and labour saving and high level of automation. A 30 m³ oven can treat 1.5 tonne of straw within 24 hours. The energy consumed per tonne of straw is less than 100 kWh, with a cost of ¥ 29 (in 1990), equivalent to the daily wage of two persons.

Steam is a convenient source of heat on cattle farms equipped with steam sterilizers. Oven temperature depends on steam pressure and supply time.

Generally, oven temperature is maintained with steam at 70°C for 10-12 hours, then the straw is kept in the oven for a further 22-24 hours. Considering only the coal used, the cost of steam is only 40 percent of electricity.

A built up oven, heated with coal and steam, is shown in Figure 6-28. Its walls, top and bottom are constructed with bricks, cement and insulating material. The straw trolley can be pulled in and out. At one end of the oven, a stove is built in a pit. The tank, situated above the stove, provides the water for steam generation. The hot air flows through the main channel (3) from one end to another, turns to the second channel, returns to the main channel again and is finally released via the chimney (4). The oven is equipped with a straw trolley, wheel tracks and hard rubber wheels. When hard rubber wheels are used, the straw trolley is easily moved for loading/unloading. Rails are used for guiding when loading and unloading.

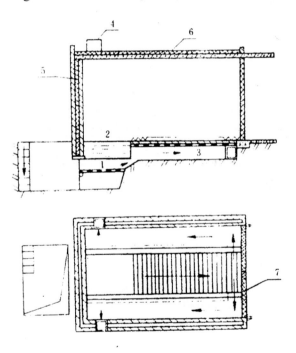

Figure 6-28. Ammoniation oven heated by coal and steam

KEY: 1. Stove; 2. Water tank; 3. Smoke channel; 4. Chimney; 5. Insulation; 6. Insulated top; 7. Insulated door.

In coal producing areas such as Shanxi province, heat from coal is ten times cheaper than from electricity. It is a convenient fuel for regions with sufficient supplies and cheaper labour.

Heat-explosion equipment

The principles of heat-explosion combine heat reaction and mechanical processing. Under the action of steam at 170°C, straw lignin is broken down and partly hydrolyzed. During the explosion, the particles impact each other inside the tube and at the same time the water trapped within cells rapidly expands to a gaseous state and physically tears apart the brittle cell wall. Straw is shredded into fine particles, greatly increasing its surface area. The quality of the treated straw is considerably improved. Equipment and a flow chart of the technology is shown in Figure 6-29.

After cutting by the chopper (1), the material is transported via the storing bin (2), the hopper (3) and charging valve (4) to pressure container (5). After being sealed, the container (5) is injected with low or medium pressure steam to a pressure of 0.5-1.0 MPa, supplied by the burner (6) and controlled by the discharge valve (7), and maintained at this high pressure for some time (from 1 to 30 minutes). The pressure is then abruptly released through the rotating ball valve (9), and the material discharged into container (10) through tube (8), for subsequent direct feeding or pelleting.

The cost of this equipment was ¥ 65 000 in 1990. The volume of the pressure container is 0.9 m³. Straw output is 300 – 400 kg/hour, coal consumed is ca 50 kg/hour, and the cost for treating 1 kg of straw is about ¥ 0.02.

After heat-explosion, the physical properties of the straw have been changed, and the intake of the entire crop is increased by 50 to 90 percent. The digestibility is increased more than 50 percent. The heat explosion treatment can eliminate the toxins of colza (rapeseed) and cottonseed cakes, and sterilize the faeces of chicken, duck and cattle to odourless materials.

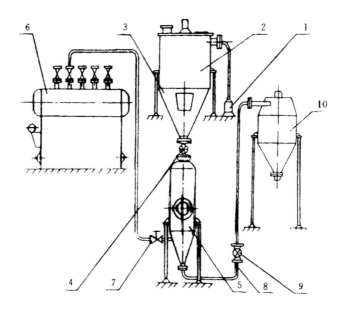

Figure 6-29. Heat-explosion equipment

KEY: 1. Chopper; 2. Storage bin; 3. Feed hopper; 4. Feed valve; 5. Pressure container; 6. Boiler; 7. Inlet steam valve; 8. Discharge tube; 9. Discharge valve; 10. Storage container.

AMMONIATION WITH ANHYDROUS AMMONIA

Injection equipment

The full set of the ammonia injection equipment (Figure 6-30), developed by the Non-conventional Feed Institute of China Agricultural University, consists of an ammonia bottle, a high pressure hose, a flow meter, a low pressure hose (rubber hose) and an ammonia spear. Protective equipment (gas mask, rubber gloves and boots) must be used.

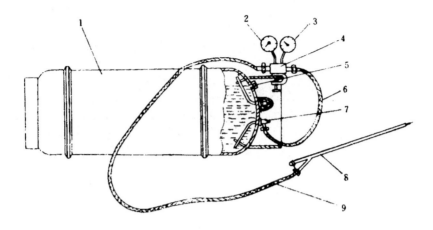

Figure 6-30. Ammonia application equipment

KEY: 1. Ammonia bottle; 2. Low pressure meter; 3. High pressure meter; 4. Flow meter; 5. Safety plug; 6. High pressure hose; 7. Valve; 8 Injecting spear; 9. Low pressure hose.

During treatment, the ammonia bottle should be laid horizontally, keeping vertically the line connecting the two valves: the upper for gas and the lower for liquid. One end of the high-pressure hose is connected to the lower valve and the other end to the high pressure end of the flow meter. One end of the low pressure hose is connected to the low pressure end of the flow meter and the other end to the ammonia spear.

After connecting the full set, operators should first put on their protective equipment: gas mask, rubber gloves, boots and suit. Second, the ammonia spear is inserted into the straw stack, about 0.5 m from the ground. Third, the lower valve is slowly unscrewed to inject the appropriate dose of ammonia according to the amount of straw. When finished, the valve is closed, but the spear kept in place for 4-5 minutes to allow ammonia left in the hose and spear to flow to the straw. Finally, the spear is pulled from the stack and the injection hole sealed with glue or tied with a string.

Using the flow meter, ammonia can be injected into the stack directly from an ammonia truck, avoiding ammonia transfer from tank to bottle. As a result, working efficiency is increased.

Construction of an ammoniation station

Anhydrous ammonia is the cheapest ammonia source, and, for this reason, treating straw with anhydrous ammonia has been advocated. However, aqueous ammonia is toxic, volatilizes easy and causes burns, thus pressure containers are required for transport and storage. It is necessary to build an anhydrous ammonia supply system. Considering the practical radius of service and amount to be used, a county-level ammoniation station might be needed. Functions of the station are to obtain ammonia in large quantities from chemical (usually fertilizer) factories in tank trucks, store it in large containers, distribute it in bottles and also to perform the injection into the straw at farmer level. At the same time, the station also can market other ammonia sources (e.g. urea) and ammoniation equipment.

Selection of equipment for transport and storage

Many types of transport and storage facilities for anhydrous ammonia have been manufactured in China, including ammonia tank trucks, containers and bottles, some of which are listed in Table 6-7. The 3-ton Dongfeng truck tank and the 7.2-ton Hongyan 19 truck tank have been selected as the main models to meet requirements in a flexible manner. Anhydrous ammonia containers are mainly used in ammoniation stations connected with an ammonia supply system. When selecting ammonia containers, cost and uniformity of ammonia delivery should be taken into account. Because anhydrous ammonia can be transferred directly from a tank placed on a truck body into bottles, tanks may not be required for a county-level ammoniation station if funding is adequate.

Table 6-7. Equipment sizes for ammonia transport and storage

Category	Type	Capacity
Anhydrous ammonia tank trucks	Dongfeng	3.0 t
	Dongfeng-13	5.1 t
	Hongyan-19	7.2 t
	Hongyan-30	12.0 t
Anhydrous ammonia containers	6 m^3	3 t
	16 m^3	8 t
	25 m^3	12.5 t
	50 m^3	25 t
Bottles	800 litre	400 kg
	400 litre	200 kg
	40 litre	20 kg

When selecting ammonia bottles, the first factor to be considered is convenience for loading and unloading. Because hand tractors or small carts can easily transport a 400-litre (200 kg) ammonia bottle, they have been selected as the main type. The 40-litre (20 kg) bottles are well adapted for farmers ammoniating straw in stacks, because of their easy transport, loading and unloading. One 40-litre bottle can treat 700 kg of straw in a stack, avoiding weighing and other complex procedures, and it can be transported by bicycle. The Non-conventional Feed Institute of China Agricultural University and relevant factories have promoted the "one bottle, one stack" concept based on this small bottle, as recommended by FAO experts.

Ammonia transfer

One of the important roles of the ammoniation station is to transfer anhydrous ammonia from the truck tank to bottles. If the liquid level in the tank is nearly equal to that in the bottle, ammonia can not flow by gravity and a compressor is needed. Ammonia compressors are available in Denmark. In China, an ammonia compressor has been obtained by redesigning the corrosion-prone parts of an air compressor.

The Non-conventional Feed Institute of China Agricultural University has successfully developed an anhydrous ammonia flow meter. The system of transferring ammonia from truck tank to bottle is shown in Figure 6-31. The ammonia transferring procedure is:

- A high-pressure hose is attached between the liquid valve on the truck tank and the bottles. A gas hose is attached between the gas valve on the truck tank and bottle through the compressor.
- The gas valve on the truck tank is opened and checked for any leakages (splits or cracks along the hose).
- The bottle's gas valve is opened, then the truck tank's valve, and a check is made for leakage along the hoses.
- The liquid valve on the bottle is then opened.
- The compressor to transfer ammonia from the truck tank to the bottle is started before the liquid is released into the hose.

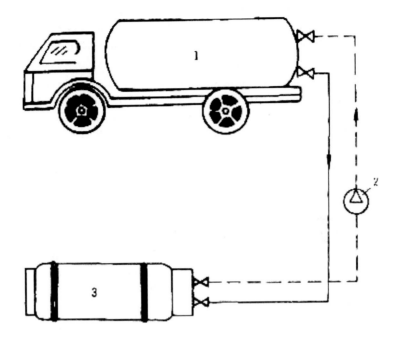

Figure 6-31. The transfer system from the truck tank to the ammonia bottle

KEY: 1. Ammonia truck tank; 2. Ammonia compressor; 3. Ammonia bottle.

It is better to place an ammonia pressure meter on the bottle's gas valve, and to compare its value with that on the tank. If the pressure of the tank is consistently more than that of bottle, this means the system is working fine.

Layout of ammoniation station

Determining service scale and equipment. The technology of treating straw with anhydrous ammonia is already mature. The ammonia dosage should be 3 percent of the straw dry weight. It is estimated that 1.5 tonne of ammoniated straw are enough for one head of cattle a year. Table 6-8 is based on an assumption of 1.5 tonne per head per year, and 300 working days for the ammoniation station a year. Table 6-7 indicates that a farm with 10 000 beef cattle needs 15 000 tonne of ammoniated straw, requiring 450 tonne of anhydrous ammonia annually. The quantity of ammoniated straw and ammonia for other animal species can be estimated by converting other livestock units into cattle units. The type and number of ammoniation facilities are determined by the quantity of anhydrous ammonia needed per year. The number of trips is estimated based on truck tank size and distance between the station and the fertilizer factory.

Table 6-8. Relationship between cattle number, straw amount, anhydrous ammonia and facilities required

Cattle	Treated straw (ton/yr)	NH₃ need[1] (ton/yr)	Trips of 3-ton tank truck		Trips of 7.2-ton tank truck		No. of 200-kg bottles needed
			Per year	Per day	Per year	Per day	
10 000	15 000	450	150	0.5	62.5	0.200	15
20 000	30 000	900	300	1.0	125.0	0.420	30
30 000	45 000	1 350	450	1.5	187.5	0.625	45
40 000	60 000	1 800	600	2.0	250.0	0.830	60
50 000	75 000	2 250	750	2.5	312.5	1.040	75
60 000	90 000	2 700	900	3.0	375.0	1.250	90
70 000	105 000	3 150	1 050	3.5	437.5	1.460	105
80 000	120 000	3 600	1 200	4.0	500.0	1.670	120
90 000	135 000	4 050	1 350	4.5	562.5	1.875	135
100 000	150 000	4 500	1 500	5.0	625.0	2.080	150

NOTES: (1) As anhydrous ammonia.

The total volume of bottles should be double that of the tank to ensure thorough discharge. That means that half of the bottles will be with farmers and the other half on station. The bottles should be recycled to accelerate turnover and improve working efficiency. In addition, small ammonia bottles holding 40 litre (20 kg) should also be available to facilitate farm work. At the station, ammonia is transferred from the truck to bottles through a hose controlled by a platform scale. Because the amount of ammonia remaining in each bottle varies, it is impossible to estimate the total amount transferred by a flow meter. At the same time, the amount in each bottle is an important consideration for safe transport, so flow meters are unsuitable for stations.

Equipment and its cost. Equipment and its cost in a typical ammoniation station serving 20 000 beef cattle are listed in Tables 6-8 and 6-9. The ammoniation of 30 000 tonne of straw requires 900 tonne of anhydrous ammonia, which can be transported by a 3-ton truck tank once daily (Table 6-7). At the same time, 30 small bottles with 200 kg and other facilities, such as a farm vehicle, a small four-wheel tractor and trailer, are also needed. Appropriate schemes can be planned for various sizes of ammoniation stations, based on the data in Table 6-9.

Table 6-9. Equipment and cost for an ammoniation station serving 20 000 cattle

Equipment item	Number needed	Cost per unit (¥ 10 000)	Total cost (¥ 10 000)
3-ton truck with ammonia tank	1	6.95	6.95
200-kg anhydrous ammonia bottle	30	0.20	6.00
Farm vehicle	1	4.50	4.50
Weighing scale (500 kg capacity)	1	0.05	0.05
Loading and unloading frame	1	0.20	0.20
Small four-wheel tractor	1	0.70	0.70
Trailer for small four-wheel tractor	1	0.25	0.25
Hand trolley	1	0.05	0.05
Other			0.50
Total			19.20

Personnel. For a typical ammoniation station serving 20-50 000 cattle, 5-7 persons are needed (1 manager, 2 drivers, 2-4 operators).

Construction requirements and plan layout. Each ammoniation station should be designed specifically for the service scale and land and equipment available. An ammoniation station for a 20-50 000-cattle catchment (typical county level) shows typical construction requirements and layout (see Figure 6-32). The area is 40 ¥ 40 m (1 600 m²). In order to quickly transfer ammonia from the tank truck to bottles, the difference in height between tank and bottle should be adequate. Thus, a 1-m platform (10) is suitable for loading and unloading. It has an inspection pit for checking or repairing vehicles. The platform can also be used for general loading and unloading operations. A shed beside the platform (8) holds 125 ammonia bottles (200 kg each), standing vertically. At the end of shed (8) there is a storeroom (9) with a separate wall. A tractor can be driven close to shed (8). One person can load and unload with the aid of a movable gallows frame. The office (1) is used as a check point and for sales (urea, ammonia filling equipment and plastic sheets). The other rooms are an office (2), a meeting room and manager's office, living rooms (3), toilet (4), large (5) and small (6) garages and stores for urea, ammonia filling equipment and plastic sheets (7). (11) are flower beds, and (12) are trees.

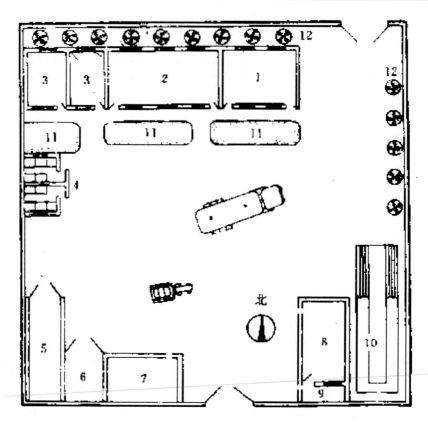

Figure 6-32. County-level ammoniation station

The living and administrative areas are located at the corner opposite to the ammonia source to minimize effects on people. Doors on opposite sides of the compound facilitate access of trucks and tractors. The whole yard is large enough for vehicles to turn around without the need to reverse.

A typical budget for the construction of a county-level ammoniation station is given in Table 6-10.

Table 6-10. Budget for construction of a county-level ammoniation station

Building	Size (m)	Unit price (¥)	No.	Total cost (¥)
Office and dormitory	3.0 × 6.0	3 000	7	21 000
Truck garage	3.5 × 11.0	5 000	1	5 000
Car garage	4.5 × 6.5	3 500	1	3 500
Shed for urea storage	9.0 × 6.5	6 000	1	6 000
Platform for loading and unloading	15.0 × 4.0 × 1.0	3 000	1	3 000
Shed for ammonia bottles	3.0 × 11.0	5 000	1	5 000
Toilet	4.5 × 6.0	1 000	1	1 000
Road, water and electricity facilities				10 000
Total				54 500

Economic assessment. The cost estimation is done taking into account the following factors:

- Depreciation of equipment and buildings over 10 years
- Wages at ¥ 250 per person per month
- Transport costs of ¥ 0.03/ton/km
- 5% profit on turnover
- Aqueous ammonia cost of ¥ 1.4/kg

The economics of a county-level ammoniation station serving 20 000 cattle are presented in Table 6-11. The price of aqueous ammonia reached ¥ 0.1434/kg after transport, storage and distribution by the ammoniation station. Except for personnel wages and transport fees, other costs were ¥ 87 050 per year. Investment in equipment and building construction was ¥ 24 500. It is estimated that 3 years are needed to recover the investment. The cost of buying the land and electricity also should be taken into account. In addition, possible additional income from sales of urea, ammonium bicarbonate and ammonia equipment is not considered.

Table 6-11. Economics of a county-level ammoniation station for 20 000 cattle

Cost	Yearly depreciation		Wages	Transport cost	Profit	Total
	Equipment	Buildings				
Total	45 250	4 850	21 000	67 500	157 000	
Per kg of aqueous ammonia	0.1213	0.0054	0.0167	0.0300	0.0700	0.1434

NOTE: (1) Aqueous ammonia sold annually is 900 tonne. (2) All values are in ¥

County-level ammoniation station in parallel to the ammonia supply system in a fertilizer factory. Such a station can be built on an empty area inside or close to the fertilizer factory. A tank, with a volume 5 times that of expected daily use, can be connected to the ammonia source in the factory. The capacity for ammonia delivery can be increased with a larger tank, but the cost also increases. For a station serving 20 000 cattle, a 12.5 tonne tank is preferred. It costs about ¥ 52 000. Having a station associated with the fertilizer factory saves not only on transport but also on wages and building cost. The economic assessment can be done on a similar basis to that above.

Township-level ammoniation station. Such an ammoniation station would be responsible for supplying ammonia for straw ammoniation. It can be part of the agricultural machinery service system or can be contracted to a professional farmer. Most of the equipment required, listed in Table 6-12, can be shared with the agricultural machinery station.

Table 6-12. Equipment for a township-level ammoniation station

Equipment item	No. needed	Unit cost (¥)	Total cost (¥)
Small four-wheel tractor	1	7 000	7 000
Trailer for tractor	1	2 500	2 500
200 kg ammonia bottle	2	2 000	4 000
Ammonia filling and protective equipment	1	750	750
Weighing scale (500 kg capacity)	1	500	500
Total			14 750

The village-level ammoniation station requires 3 persons (¥ 200/month each). The running cost for a small four-wheel tractor is ¥ 30/day. Anhydrous ammonia sales are 400 kg a day, or 120 tonne a year. The depreciation of equipment is calculated over 10 years. Cost of anhydrous ammonia handling is ¥ 0.147/kg.

Assuming that the cost for transport and storage of anhydrous ammonia is ¥ 0.227/kg for county and township-level ammoniation stations, and that 1 kg of anhydrous ammonia can treat 33.3 kg of straw, then the cost of treated straw is ¥ 8.3/ton. This estimation is based on general 1998 prices. When planning an ammoniation station, the economic assessment should be based on local costs.

SAFETY OPERATION OF ANHYDROUS AMMONIA EQUIPMENT

Treating straw with anhydrous ammonia has many advantages, such as high efficiency, low cost, simplicity of operation and elimination of parasite eggs and weed seeds. However, anhydrous ammonia is toxic and explosive, so pressure containers are required for transport and storage. It is very important to follow relevant national regulations for safe operation. The basis of these regulations should be well understood. Explosions of ammonia containers happen occasionally and have resulted in persons injured or even killed. All persons working with ammonia must learn from these accidents.

Physical and chemical characteristics of ammonia, and safe operation

Ammonia is a colourless gas with suffocating and penetrating odour. Under pressure or at low temperature (-33 °C) it condenses to a clear liquid. The physical and chemical characteristics of ammonia are:

- Chemical formula NH_3
- Boiling point (at atmospheric pressure)   -33.4°C
- Density of ammonia   0.596
- Density of anhydrous ammonia   0.617 (at 20°C)
- Solubility in water (at 15°C)   60 g/100 g H_2O
- Vapour from 1 litre of anhydrous ammonia   1 000 litre
- Solubility of gas in 1 litre of water   700 litre (20°C)
- Explosion limits   15-28% (volume)
- Safe concentration   0.0001 mg/litre
- Toxic concentration   0.2 mg/litre

In the presence of water or steam, copper, zinc and aluminium, and alloys containing these metals, will be corroded by ammonia. These metals are therefore not to be used in ammonia equipment.

The pressure change in an ammonia container according to temperature is illustrated in Figure 6-33.

LIQUID
PHASE

GASEOUS
PHASE

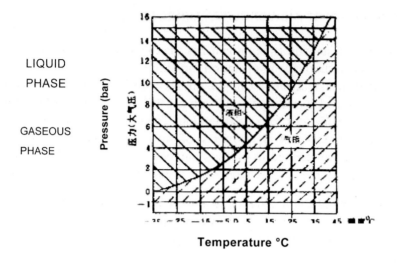

Temperature °C

Figure 6-33. Ammonia pressure change with temperature

The chemical and physical characteristics of ammonia are the basis of the selection of ammoniation equipment and for safe operation:

- From Figure 6-33 it can be seen that the ammonia pressure is $2x10^5$, $5.3x10^5$ and $14.8x10^5$ Pa for temperatures of -10, 10 and 40°C, which correspond to normal winter, spring and autumn temperature in Beijing, respectively. According to regulations, the ammonia should not be used at temperature over 50°C, equivalent to a pressure of $2.07x10^6$ Pa. Other factors are taken into account, and the design pressure for a truck tank is $2.2x10^6$ Pa and $3x10^6$ Pa for a bottle. Pressurized containers should not be exposed to the sun for a long period, nor be brought near fire.

- Ammonia easily dissolves in water, a very important consideration in safety protection and accidents. On handling sites, enough water should be available, preferably tap water. A sign indicating "safety water" must be clearly displayed. If ammonia gets into the eyes or on the skin, it should be rinsed immediately with abundant water. If ammonia leaks into the air, water spray should be used to "knock down" the vapour. Spraying polluted areas with water reduces gas emission. Covering the nose with a wet towel is an efficient method of protection.

- Ammonia's density is lower than air density. If a large amount of ammonia is released to the air, people should rapidly leave the polluted area, moving into the wind. When driving out air from an ammonia container, the gas outlet valve should be in a low position.
- The boiling point of anhydrous ammonia is -33.34°C. When anhydrous ammonia vaporizes, a great amount of heat is absorbed. If the heat source is not sufficient, the process of volatilization is slowed down; and ammonia will remain liquid for longer. If anhydrous ammonia comes into contact with the skin, temperature will decrease and water will be absorbed, causing injury. If a great amount of ammonia liquid escapes from a damaged valve, if possible a soil or sand dam or a dig pit should be made around the discharge (because the ammonia boiling off will cool surfaces to -33.34°C) to reduce gas emission. Heat absorption from the air can be further reduced by spraying foam on the liquid ammonia, or simply covering it with a plastic sheet.
- If it is impossible to dig a hole or to make a dam, the container should be rapidly turned so that the damaged valve is uppermost (from liquid to gas position), thereby reducing the speed of ammonia release, since 1 litre of anhydrous ammonia will vaporize into 1 000 litre of ammonia gas.
- When the ammonia content in the air gets to 15-28 percent, it has reached the explosion limit. Below 15 percent, there is not enough ammonia for the explosion, and above 28 percent there is not enough oxygen. In practice, ammonia in the air or in containers should be kept below the explosion limit. For new ammonia containers or for those that have not been used for a long time, it is necessary to drive air out before using them. Adding a little ammonia into the container and opening the lower valve, the gas is pushed out into water through the hose. Repeating the process several times until there are no more bubbles in the water means that all discharged gas is ammonia. Since ammonia dissolves rapidly and thoroughly in water, in order to prevent air from going into ammonia containers, a little ammonia should be left in the bottle: that is to say, the pressure meter should remain at 0.05 MPa (0.5 atmospheres pressure). In addition, avoid fire on the handling sites to prevent explosions and self-ignition at 630°C. Attention should be paid during welding or repairing ammonia containers: ammonia should be purged beforehand.

- Containers should not be filled to excess. Figure 6-33 clearly shows that the vaporizing pressure increases with temperature. If the container is completely full of ammonia, with no empty space for liquid expansion with increasing temperature, the pressure will increases at the rate of 1.5×10^6 Pa/°C. If the temperature increases by 5°C, an explosion will occur. The amount of ammonia to be put in a container (G) should be calculated using the formula: $G = 0.53V$, where V represents the real volume of the container (in litres) and 0.53 is the maximum filling factor (kg/litre).

Safety supervision of ammonia containers

In order to emphasize the management of pressure containers with explosion risk, *Safety supervision regulations for gas bottles*, *Supervision regulations for pressure containers*, and *Management regulations for liquefied gas tank trucks* have been promulgated by the National Council, the Ministry of Work and Personnel, and the Ministry of Chemical Industry. Clear regulations have been established for the design, manufacture, installation, usage and inspection or repair of pressure containers, as well as for reporting accidents.

Ammonia tank trucks and bottles are classed as medium-pressure container transport. As ammonia is very toxic, a container of more than 440 litre volume is a class II container, which can implies serious consequences in a explosion.

According to national regulations, the following points should be observed when using pressure containers:

- *Inspection and acceptance.* The design and manufacturing company must have a Certificate of Approval from the appropriate authorities, and the products must have a quality certificate.
- *Keeping technical records.* Detailed records should be kept, including dates, inspections, repairs, measures taken to resolve problems, and so on.
- *Personnel training.* Operators must be trained, and receive the required qualification after passing an examination.
- *Care in handling.* Valves should be opened slowly to prevent pressure from rising or falling too quickly.
- *Avoid overfilling.* Do not overfill, to avoid high pressure and temperature.
- *Regular inspection.* According to the specifications of the pressure containers, they should be inspected externally once a year and internally once every two years by the relevant authorities. After inspection, a visible and permanent label of the authority, with the year of inspection, must be affixed to the container.

- *Safe transport*. Ammonia containers should be protected from impacts or overturning. Valves should be closed and caps well screwed on during transport. Loading and unloading must be done slowly. Ammonia containers should never be placed together with other containers, especially oxygen bottles. Fire extinguishers must be available.
- *Regular maintenance*. Pressure containers must be repaired and maintained regularly to prevent leaking. They should be kept in dry areas when not used.
- *Qualified drivers and operators*. The drivers and operators of tank trucks must be trained and qualify by passing an examination. Moving and stopping ammonia tank trucks should respect not only normal traffic regulations but also special conditions. The relevant regulations should be written and displayed in the appropriate position in or on the vehicle.
- *Accident reporting*. Any accident should be reported immediately to the relevant administration, police and labour department.

Regulations for safety in straw ammoniation
Ammonia is toxic and may explode under certain conditions. The ammonia containers are classed as "pressure containers with risk of explosion." Treating straw with anhydrous ammonia can endanger life and health if not done correctly. It is therefore necessary to follow the precautions and regulations made by the Bureau of Animal Production and Health (MOA, 1990):

Safety operation regulations for straw ammoniation
- Operators must have the necessary training, pass the examination and obtain their qualification.
- Safety equipment available at the working site should include:
  - an abundant supply of fresh water;
  - filter masks with ammonia filters;
  - gloves and boots made of rubber or another suitable material; and
  - fire extinguishers.
- Each new ammonia container must have an accompanying quality certificate that is properly filed.
- Never overfill whenever adding ammonia to a container.
- In summer, do not put ammonia containers in the sun. In winter, if ammonia flow is low, move containers to a warm place. Never heat them with fire.

- During ammonia transport, storage and straw ammoniation, check containers and hoses for leakage or swollen parts. Stop operation to make appropriate repairs to damage if found.
- Ammonia bottles must be firmly secured to the vehicle during transport to prevent them from falling due to movement.
- Be sure not to hit or to roll ammonia bottles during loading and unloading, which should be done slowly.
- Screw and tighten valves during bottle transportation and storage.
- Transport of anhydrous ammonia and oxygen in same wagon and storage in the same shed is strictly prohibited to avoid danger of explosion.
- If there is still pressure in a container, do not repair or fasten any part under pressure.
- When ammoniating straw, first place the spear into straw, then open the valve.
- Open and close ammonia-injecting valves slowly. During ammonia injection the gas pressure must be below 0.8 Pa. Do not hit the ammonia bottle with any tool.
- Ammonia flow should stop when pressure drops to 0.05 Pa.
- The ammonia containers can not be used to store any other material without the written consent of the working department.
- Ammonia containers must be checked regularly.
- The operators must wear protective equipment, including rubber gloves and protective suit, and stand upwind from the ammonia source.
- If ammonia leaks to the air, people should lay down on the ground, cover their noses with a wet towel and move upwind.
- Fire is forbidden in the vicinity of the ammonia station and the site of straw ammoniation.
- If an accident occurs, it should be immediately reported to administration and labour departments.

Chapter 7

Economic analysis of animal production based on crop resides

Zhang Cungen
China Academy of Agricultural Sciences

INTRODUCTION

The economic benefits of using untreated and treated crop residues as feed for ruminants mainly depends on the source and cost of crop residues, cost of treatment, cost of urea or other ammonia source, on the price of protein supplements, as well as on agricultural production and technical levels and other factors. In relation to the potential of crop residue use, countries can be divided into four types:

Type 1 are developing countries and regions with a high population density. Most countries in the Far East and part of the Middle East belong to this group. Crop residues in general are used as the major feed for ruminants. Treated crop residues may result in very good economic returns.

Type 2 are developing countries and regions with low population density. Most countries and regions in Africa and Latin America where land use is not restricted belong to this type. Feed supply comes from various sources, but cattle production relies, in general, on natural pastures. Crop residues, treated or untreated in emergency situations, especially in the dry season, become an important feed resource.

Type 3 are developed countries and regions with an ample grain supply. The USA, Canada and France belong to this type. In addition to roughage, ruminants are fed with large quantities of concentrates to obtain high yields of animal products. Untreated crop residues are sometimes used as a source of fibre substituting hay or silage. Under these conditions, treated crop residues might give fairly good economic benefits. However, it might not be economical to utilize crop residues in areas where the production of hay or silage is high.

Type 4 are the developed countries and regions with small land area per capita. Most countries in north Europe belong to this type. In order to achieve self-sufficiency in food, the governments of these countries attach great importance to the utilization of crop residues so as to increase food output from the limited land. Among north European countries, Denmark and Norway use the highest proportion of crop residues as feed.

In China, the broad agricultural region, characterized by huge population with limited land, belongs to Type 2. It has good prospects for developing animal husbandry based on crop residues.

STATUS OF THE UTILIZATION OF CROP RESIDUES IN CHINA

In general, straw is used for burning, composting, paper making and animal husbandry. For a long period in the past, due to limited economic development and way of life, it was very popular to use straw as fuel for cooking. It is estimated that 70 percent of total straw was used as fuel. With the improvement in the rural economy and farmers' living standards, rural energy has become diversified to coal, natural gas, biogas, electricity, etc., so the amount of straw used as fuel has been reduced to less than 50 percent. Direct straw application to soils is also practised, but this operation increases the cost by about ¥ 10 per mu (¥ 150/ha). At the same time, it takes time for straw to fully decompose, thus interfering with germination and growth of the next crop. This is particularly true in regions with intensive agriculture because it increases the difficulties for crop rotation. In addition, returning straws directly to the field may have hidden dangers in terms of insects and diseases, so this utilization has its limitations. Returning straw to fields wastes the energy, decomposed by micro-organisms, while crops can only utilize part of the N, P, K and other inorganic nutrients after decomposition.

Another use for straw is as raw material for paper making. It is estimated that 2-2.5 tonne of rice straw can be processed into 1 tonne of paper. However, it is difficult to collect due to the large volumes involved and its disperse distribution, and only part of the rice straw can be utilized. Since 1995, the State has shut down many medium- and small-sized local paper plants due to environmental pollution. The closure has led to a surplus of straw.

In many regions of China, large amounts of unused crop residues are piled up by field edges and road sides, and extensive burning of straw by farmers in the fields occurs every autumn at harvest. This has caused a drop in soil organic matter, hardening and producing impervious soils with low moisture holding capacity. It has also caused atmospheric pollution and poor air visibility. In May 1997, due to smoke produced by burning of wheat straw, the Chengdu Shuangliu Airport was closed for 4 hours. Visibility had dropped below the minimum safety limits required for flying. Twenty-two flights had to be diverted to another airfield and eight flights were delayed. At Hebei Shijiazhuang Airport there were also flight delays, and on the Jinan-Qingdao motorway there was an increase in traffic accidents, both due to the burning of crop residues. Therefore, each province has set regulations strictly prohibiting the burning of straw, but straw burning still occurs, despite regulations and repeated disciplinary action. It is estimated that about 40 to 45 percent of the crop residues are still used as fuel or burned on the hillsides yearly, equivalent to over 1.2 million tonne of N, 280 000 tonne of P and 2.8 million tonne of K (Table 7-1), resulting in both environmental pollution and energy waste. In these regions, straw has become a significant cause of environmental pollution.

Table 7-1. Nutrition elements in straw

Year	Straw output ($\times 10^6$ tonne)	Nitrogen ($\times 10^4$ tonne)	Phosphorus ($\times 10^4$ tonne)	Potassium ($\times 10^4$ tonne)	NPK as proportion of total chemical fertilizer output of China
1997	600	300	70	700	25 %

SOURCE: Lu Ming, 1998.

One of the best methods to prevent environment pollution caused by straw is to develop livestock production based on straw and to return manure to the fields. In other words, turn the organic and inorganic nutrients contained in straw into high quality products (meat, milk, skin, wool) and bio-energy (animal power) via ruminants. The manure, which can not be directly utilized by humans, can be returned to farmland. Most of the nutrients needed by crops can be met by animal manure. Long-term applications of manure can increase soil organic matter and improve soil structure and fertility, which are beneficial for the establishment of a highly efficient virtuous circle of agricultural production and ecology. If manure is used to generate biogas via fermentation as a source of rural energy, and the effluents returned to farmland, the energy flow would become even more rational.

Chinese farmers have a tradition of using straw to feed herbivores, for example, chopped straw for cattle. However, scientific experiments have shown that chopping or milling can not improve straw digestibility: it can only increase intake and reduce feeding losses. In the past, most cattle farmers used animal traction and fed straw and other roughage during slack seasons and some concentrates during busy seasons. In this case, cattle could not develop strong body condition and used to be called "old yellow cattle" at the end of their lives. Cattle with less flesh was a direct result of this production method. At present, animal draft power has been gradually replaced by machinery and animal numbers. However, the improvement of cattle should not only be put on the agenda, but also on the work plans, since it is absolutely possible to obtain meat from cattle.

Turning draught cattle into beef cattle is not simply a change in the feeding objective; matched feeding methods must be implemented. The recently proposed strategy of "relying on science and technology for the utilization of straw at a higher level for the development of herbivorous animals" depends on innovative feeding methods. The two projects on developing cattle production based on straw as the major feed, undertaken by FAO in 1990 and 1992, achieved their desired objectives.

Experts from FAO recommended cattle production based on straw as a low-concentrate and long-cycle feeding system. In other words, it aimed to take advantage of the digestion characteristics of ruminants, and particularly the fact that straw in China is a non-commercial feed in most cases, to use more roughage and less concentrates to obtain a market animal through a long-cycle finishing process. Straw was used as roughage, and processed and treated with ensiling and ammoniating technologies as major methods. It was essential to profit from this opportunity to develop a new alternative for straw utilization work in China.

With the intention of taking advantage of the rich straw resources of the country, the State started the demonstration projects *Developing livestock production with straw and returning manure to fields, after digestion by livestock* in the large agricultural regions in 1992. The project had found a practical way to reduce straw burning. In the short period of 8 years, important advances were achieved. The extension of ensiling and ammoniating technologies has obviously accelerated the rate of straw utilization in China. In general, once crops mature, the straw has become dry and inappropriate for making silage. In this case, ammoniation is the way to improve the nutritional value of straw. China started late in the extension of straw ammoniating technology (1985) and did not undertake the basic research and experimentation until the early 1980s, but in comparatively few years the country made significant progress in straw ammoniation. Thus, total straw feeding increased from 20 percent in 1992 to 28 in 1996. The utilization of treated straw rose from 4.2 to 9.5 percent. In 1996, a total of 85.2 million tonne of silage and 80.5 million tonne of ammoniated straw were made in China. Based on the equivalence of 5 kg of ammoniated maize stalk or 2.5 kg of ammoniated wheat straw in N content to 1 kg of maize, more than 20 million tonne of grain had been saved. The feeding rate of straw in Hebei Province reached 49 percent in 1997. This included 6.93 million tonne of silage (fresh weight) and 2.45 million tonne of ammoniated straw. In other words, about half of the straw in the whole province was utilized for livestock. This played an important role in alleviating environmental pollution caused by burning. Table 7-2 shows the situation of straw utilization in pilot counties and villages.

Table 7-2. Straw utilization in pilot counties and villages

Place	Year	Farm area ($\times 10^3$ mu)	End-of-year population ($\times 10^4$)	Cattle marketed ($\times 10^4$/yr)	Straw dry matter ($\times 10^4$ tonne)			Fed as % of all straw
					Output	Fed	Ensiled & treated	
Shandong Province								
Yucheng county	1997	803.3	22	12	100	40	33	40
Maozhuang village	1997	1.2	0.06	0.03	2.08	1	0.04	48
Tangwang village	1997	1.6	0.08	0.04	2.77	1.2	0.04	45
Hebei Province								
All province	1997	98 000	661.7	429.6	3 000	1 470	200	49
Sanhe county	1998	530	11.13	17.19	66	34.5	20	52
Henan Province								
Huaiyang county	1992	951.1	22.6	6.45	118.4	54.4	1.32	46

SOURCES: The Animal Husbandry Bureau of Yucheng County; the Animal Husbandry Bureau of Henan Province; Animal Husbandry Bureau of Sanhe County.

PROGRESS ON DEVELOPMENT OF STRAW FOR RUMINANT FEED IN CHINA

The development of cattle production nationally and in the Central Plain Provinces of Henan, Shandong, Anhui and Hebei in recent years reflects the current status, the prospects and the economic benefits of the development of livestock production based on straw in China. In these provinces, there are important agricultural regions for grain and cotton, rich in straw and cottonseed. Since 1978, when the country started to implement the open and reform policies, but especially since 1987, these provinces have extended, in a large manner, the technologies of straw ammoniating and ensiling, as well as the necessary matching feeding techniques, which has greatly promoted cattle production development. Shandong Province, for example, had invested a total of ¥ 200 000 million and 40 000 tonne of urea, and produced a total of 3.44 million tonne of ammoniated straw by 1993. Cattle have shown the fastest population growth of all animals except poultry, and these four provinces had the fastest increase. This shows that cattle production based on straw is profitable. At national level, the cattle population reached 124 million in 1998, a 73 percent increase from 1980. During the same period, the cattle population in Henan, Shandong, Anhui and Hebei Provinces nearly doubled, an increase of 15.4 percentage points in the nation (Table 7-3).

Table 7-3. Cattle population in the Central Plain Provinces 1980-1998 ($\times 10^4$ head)

	1980	1990	1998	1990/1980	1998/1980
All China	7 169	10 288	12 435	1.44	1.74
Henan	340	893	1 301	2.63	3.83
Shandong	218	512	912	2.35	4.19
Anhui	241	501	627	2.08	2.60
Hebei	121	208	665	1.72	5.51
The four provinces	919	2 133	3 504	2.32	3.81
As proportion of all China (%)	12.8	20.5	28.2	--	--

SOURCE: China Statistical Yearbook, 1997 and 1999

Second to poultry meat, beef showed the largest increase within total national meat output. China had a beef output of 4.8 million tonne in 1998, 17 times that of 1980. Beef output was 26 000 tonne in 1980 in Henan, Shandong, Anhui and Hebei Provinces, only 9.7 percent of the nation; by 1998, it had reached 2.3 million tonne, or 47.7 percent (Table 7-4), an increase of 87 times compared to a 10 times increase nationwide. This fully demonstrates the efficacy of extending the technology of developing livestock production with straw and returning manure to fields, after digestion by livestock in the four provinces.

Table 7-4. Beef output in the Central Plain provinces during 1980-1998 ($\times 10^4$ tonne)

	1980	1990	1998	1990/1980	1998/1980
All China	26.9	125.6	479.9	4.7	17.8
Henan	0.7	18.2	76.7	26.0	109.6
Shandong	0.9	17.6	60.1	19.6	66.8
Anhui	0.6	9.8	34.3	16.3	57.2
Hebei	0.4	5.6	58.0	4.7	145.0
Total for four provinces	2.6	51.2	229.1		
As proportion of all China (%)	9.7	40.8	47.7		

Extraction rate, average carcass weight and annual beef yield per head in China have much increased since 1980. In that year, extraction rate was 4.7 percent, carcass weight was 81 kg and annual yield per head was 3.8 kg. In 1990, these parameters were 10.8 percent, 115 kg and 12.5 kg, respectively, and by 1998 they were 30.7 percent, 133.5 kg and 41 kg. In 1980, the corresponding values for the four provinces were below the national average, but by 1990 they were already above (Table 7-5). These data demonstrate that the extension of technology for cattle production based on straw greatly improved production in the four provinces.

Compared with other countries, cattle production in China still has a long way to go. Dressing percentage of cattle in China is lower than in the developed countries, indicating the potential for improvement.

Table7-5. Change in beef production level in the Central Plain provinces (1980-1998)

	Marketing rate[1] (%)			Average carcass weight (kg)			Beef yield per cattle[2] (kg)		
	1980	1990	1998	1980	1990	1998	1980	1990	1998
All China	4.7	10.8	30.7	81.0	115	133	3.8	12.5	41.0
Henan	2.9	19.1	42.5	70.7	108	139	2.1	20.7	59.1
Shandong	4.0	23.3	45.9	100.9	160	169	4.1	37.2	77.7
Anhui	3.6	17.5	38.1	76.5	112	143	2.8	19.5	54.4
Hebei	4.2	22.2	61.6	74.9	124	152	3.1	27.6	93.7
4 provinces	3.5	20.0	46.0	81.8	125	150	2.8	24.9	69.0

NOTES: (1) Marketing rate = Number of cattle marketed in the year/cattle population by the end of previous year. (2) Beef yield per head = Beef output in the year/cattle population at the end of the previous year.

ECONOMICS OF CATTLE PRODUCTION ON AMMONIATED CROP RESIDUES

Cattle production based on straw is only one of the methods of cattle feeding, with certain scope and application conditions. Objective economic analysis of cattle production based on straw usually considers the factors discussed below.

Basic factors influencing the economic benefits

As a complete production system, cattle rearing based on straw has the general nature of an economic activity, i.e., inputs are first, and the comparison between input and output. Only when output is greater than input is there economic efficiency. Figure 7-1 shows the basic input and output factors in cattle production based on straw.

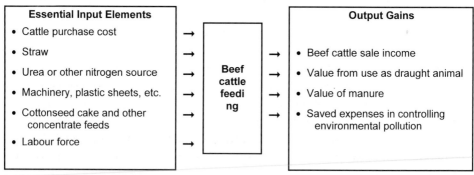

Figure 7-1. Analysis of input-output relations in cattle production based on straw

Implications of major input and output elements and their value

In order to have a complete and accurate understanding of the implications of various essential components during the process of economic analysis, the actual calculating methods for various targets are detailed below.

The benefits obtained from cattle feeding with ammoniated straw can be broken down into direct and indirect benefits. The direct benefits can be further broken down into three.

Income from beef cattle sales

The main income of cattle production is the sale of finished cattle. The key factors are dressing percentage and beef price. The former can be obtained from average values at slaughter, while the latter comes from the market. In the case of live cattle sales, the actual income is used for calculation.

Value of draught cattle

This can be calculated from the days used as a draught animal and the local daily rates; in other words, daily rate (¥/day) multiplied by the time used as draught animal (days).

Value of manure

Manure is a sort of by-product and its value should be estimated. However, it is difficult of do it in practice. After comparisons made in most areas, it is assumed that manure value is offset by labour costs.

Indirect or macro-benefits

They are savings from reduced and controlled environment pollution, reflected in social benefits. The value of these benefits has not been included in the calculations.

There are many essential inputs for cattle production based on ammoniated straw. Some of them are:

- *Cattle purchases.* It refers to the actual expense to purchase calves or cattle. In the case of calves produced by owner himself, the feed cost of the cow should be computed.
- *Cost of straw.* In general, straw cost was not included in the past. Considering the various alternative uses of straw in China, the cost of straw should be determined by the price paid by paper mills or the negotiated price during purchase.
- *Cost of urea or nitrogen source.* This cost should be derived from the actual purchase price.
- *Cost of concentrate.* When feeding ammoniated straw to cattle, some supplementary concentrate (cottonseed cake, wheat bran, etc.) is added. This cost is computed from the market price.
- *Cost of labour.* In general, surplus or slack labour is used for cattle production, and for this reason it is not included. In the case of specialized cattle raising households, the cost of labour must be included according to the wages of local agricultural labourers.
- *Cost of equipment and other items.* The investment for a cattle shed, machinery, equipment and plastic sheeting used for ammoniation should be included in production costs. It can be calculated using the formula:

Depreciation cost = Total investment/usable years

The above standard inputs and outputs provide a basis for calculating the economic benefits of cattle production based on straw, but there might be differences in application. For example, the cost or value of straw will change greatly according to time and place. In some regions, straw is regarded as waste with nearly no value, but one has to pay for harvesting, transporting and burning. In other regions, the opposite occurs. In the case of energy shortages and when there is an industrial demand, straw could be used as fuel. With the development of science and technology, straw will be attractive in new building materials and as a raw material for paper making. Therefore the opportunity cost of straw should be considered.

Estimation of economic benefits of use of crop residues for ruminants
In order to simplify the analysis of the economic benefits of cattle production with straw, the input/output ratio has been used to express the critical value of cattle production based on straw. Only when this value is greater than 1 can one can say that cattle production based on straw is effective. The larger the value, the greater the benefit. Any change in quantity or price of one of the essential factors will change the value of the input/output ratio.

On the basis of the above value, it is possible to calculate the total and daily net income per head of cattle, where:

Net income per cattle = Total income per cattle - Total input cost per cattle.

Cases influencing input/output ratio
Beef market objective
For international markets and domestic high-grade consumption, special attention should be given to beef quality. In general, this quality beef needs high-concentrate low-roughage diets for rapid finishing. Beef quality from cattle mainly fed straw will differ a lot from that produced from concentrates. The former can meet beef quality requirements of the common market, while the latter uses very little straw, just to provide the fibre needed for normal rumen function and it does not have to be chemically treated. Trade in high-grade beef is only 2-3 thousand tonne/yr; it is not discussed further here.

For the domestic market, the common cooking method is stewing (red-cooked beef, beef cooked in soy sauce, etc.), which does not require very tender beef. Therefore, this demand can be satisfied with beef coming from low-concentrate, high-roughage systems with a long finishing period. In this case, the roughage can be mainly straw, with better results if chemically treated. Only in this case does the input/output ratio have any significance.

Processing and treatment methods

There are many straw processing and treatment methods, which can be broadly divided into physical, chemical and biological. Economics should be considered when choosing the treatment method. Among the physical methods, chopping is most economical, but does not improve the nutritional value of straw. Among the chemical treatment methods, the alkalization (NaOH) method gives the best results, but the price of NaOH is high. Ammoniation also gives good results and provides non-protein nitrogen, improving the protein level of the straw. Therefore, in the situation of a general shortage of protein resources in China, the ammoniation treatment has its value. In ammoniation, anhydrous ammonia, urea or ammonium carbonate are the major ammonia resources. Anhydrous ammonia is used on large farms all year round. There are great differences in the nutritional value of untreated and ammoniated straw, as well as between ammonia sources. The price of ammonia and the benefits obtained should be carefully considered. It is essential to determine which treatment method gives the best economic benefits.

Age, body weight and breed of finishing cattle

In general, as age and size of finishing cattle increase, daily gain also increases (Table 7-6). From an economic point of view, it is an important issue to select the optimal finishing period.

Table 7-6. Relationship among initial weight, final weight and daily gain

	Daily gain (g)	Initial weight (kg)	Final weight (kg)
All test groups	713 ± 90	174	368
Best 10 cattle	894 ± 49	173	418
Heaviest 10 cattle	804 ± 100	234	453

Native yellow cattle in China have better roughage acceptance, and are more suitable for low-concentrate, high-roughage diets and long finishing periods. However, imported cattle breeds have faster growth rates and high feed requirements, and are therefore more suitable for high-concentrate, low-roughage diets for faster finishing.

Protein supplements

When adopting the low-concentrate, high-roughage route, in addition to feeding treated straws, certain levels of a protein supplement should be given to meet the growth requirement of finishing cattle. In the central plain region, cottonseed cake is an optimal protein supplement feed. This is because cottonseed cake does not need detoxification when fed to cattle and it will not compete for demand by other livestock and poultry. However, feeding too much cottonseed cake becomes uneconomical. Figure 7-2 shows the relationship between the amount of protein supplement and weight gain.

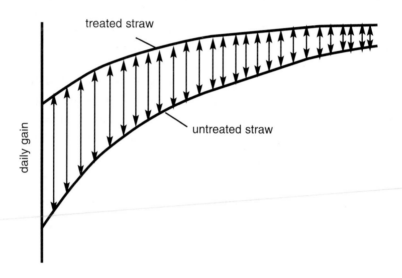

Figure 7-2. The feeding effect of treated straw vs concentrate amount

COMMENTS ON PRODUCTION STUDIES

During the period 1990 to 1992, FAO conducted studies and extension work with cattle fed on straw in Henan and Hebei Provinces. Some general comments can be made on the economic benefits of cattle production based on straw, summarizing research reports, data obtained from studies in Henan Province and related economic parameters.

Design of the study

The design of the study was feeding with ammoniated straw *ad libitum*, with different levels of protein supplement (cottonseed cake (CSC)) for native Yellow cattle, with daily gain changes observed. Table 7-7 gives the results of the experiment.

Table 7-7. Basic data of the study

Amount of cottonseed meal (kg/day/cattle)		0	1	2	3	4
Number of cattle		8	8	8	8	7
Initial weight	(kg)	182	183	183	183	183
Final weight	(kg)	205	237	242	258	262
Daily gain	(g/d)	250	660	750	845	883
Straw intake	(kg/d)	10.0	9.6	8.0	7.3	5.0

SOURCE: Dolberg and Finlayson, 1995

Analysis of economic benefits

The analysis was conducted based on input and output data of cattle raised during the finishing period (from 180 to 450 kg). The analysis was as follows according to different prices of inputs:

Case 1: CSC @ ¥ 0.4/kg and straw free

CSC ration	(kg/day)	0	1	2	3	4
Finishing weight	(kg)	270	270	270	270	270
Finishing period	(days)	1 080	450	360	320	306
Net feed consumption	(kg)	0	450	720	960	1 224
Straw intake	(tons)	1.08	4.32	2.88	2.34	1.53
Income per cattle	(¥)	1 710	1 710	1 710	1 710	1 710
Cost per cattle	(¥)	1 558	1 186	1 202	1 259	1 327
a. Concentrate cost	(¥)	0	180	288	384	480
b. Roughage cost	(¥)	618	246	146	133	87
c. Other costs	(¥)	940	760	768	742	760
Net income per head	(¥)	152	524	508	451	383
Net income per day	(¥)	0.14	1.16	1.41	1.41	1.25
Input/output ratio		1.10	1.44	1.42	1.36	1.29

NOTES: (1) Finishing weight = final weight (450 kg) minus initial weight (180 kg).
(2) Finishing period is obtained by finishing weight divided by daily gain.
(3) Live cattle sold at ¥ 3.8/kg.
(4) Cattle bought at ¥ 3.6/kg; Concentrate = cottonseed cake at ¥ 0.4/kg. For roughage, the cost of straw is not computed for the time being, only the cost of urea and plastic film used in ammoniation. The cost of urea is ¥ 0.050/kg and the cost of plastic film and labour are ¥ 0.007/kg. Other costs include: cost for buying cattle, disease control and depreciation of cattle sheds.

The net income per cattle and per day mentioned above could be used as the basis for the evaluation of cattle production based on straw. Input/output ratio provides a more comprehensive reflection of the economic benefits of cattle production based on straw. To sum up, when daily feed intake was 1 to 2 kg, better economic benefits could be achieved. When daily straw intake was 1 kg, net income per cattle and input/output ratio were highest. However, when daily straw intake was 2-3 kg, the net income per day was the best.

Case 2: CSC @ ¥ 0.4/kg and straw @ ¥ 0.06/kg

CSC	(kg/day)	0	1	2	3	4
Income per cattle	(¥)	1 710	1 710	1 710	1 710	1 710
Cost per cattle	(¥)	2 206	1 445	1 375	1 399	1 419
Net income per cattle	(¥)	-496	265	335	311	291
Net income per day	(¥)	-0.46	0.59	0.93	0.97	1.21
Input/output ratio		0.78	1.18	1.24	1.22	1.21

The results show that as the cost of straw increased from zero to ¥ 0.06/kg, a daily intake of 2-3 kg cottonseed cake gave the best economic benefits. When cottonseed cake intake was 2 kg, the best results were achieved in terms of net income per cattle and input/output ratio. However, when cottonseed cake intake was 3 kg, the highest net income per day per cattle was achieved.

The results show that as the price of CSC increased by 50 percent, a daily supplement of 1-2 kg CSC gave the best economic benefits. A daily supplement of 1 kg CSC was the best for net income per cattle and input/output ratio. A daily supplement of 2 kg CSC gave the highest net income per day per cattle. But a daily supplement of 3 kg CSC decreased the net income per day by a large margin.

Case 3: CSC increased from ¥ 0.4 to 0.6/kg and straw free

CSC intake	(kg/day)	0	1	2	3	4
Income per cattle	(¥)	1 710	1 710	1 710	1 710	1 710
Cost per cattle	(¥)	1 558	1 276	1 346	1 451	1 572
Net income per cattle	(¥)	152	434	364	259	138
Net income per day	(¥)	0.14	0.96	1.01	0.81	0.45
Input/output ratio		1.10	1.34	1.27	1.18	1.09

Case 4: CSC @ ¥ 0.6/kg and straw @ ¥ 0.06/kg

CSC intake	(kg/day)	0	1	2	3	4
Income per cattle	(¥)	1 710	1 710	1 710	1 710	1 710
Cost per cattle	(¥)	2 206	1 535	1 519	1 591	1 664
Net income per cattle	(¥)	-496	175	191	119	46
Net income per day	(¥)	-0.46	0.39	0.53	0.37	0.15
Input/output ratio		0.78	1.11	1.13	1.07	1.03

The results show that when the cost of CSC increased from ¥ 0.4 to 0.6/kg and the cost of straw increased from zero to Y 0.06/kg, i.e., all the essential inputs had reached their maximum level, a daily supplement of 2 kg CSC gave better economic benefits. Net income per day, net income per cattle and input/output ratio were all at optimal levels.

Economic analysis of different ammonia sources

The analysis above was based on use of urea, the most extensively used ammonia resource. In practice, in addition to urea, anhydrous ammonia and ammonium bicarbonate are also used. Due to their price differences, the cost of ammoniation is significantly different. On the basis of ammonia source and amount used, it is possible to calculate the cost of ammoniation per source (Table 7-8). Based on the expenses associated with each ammonia source, plus the cost of plastic sheeting and labour, the total cost per kilogram of ammoniated straw can be obtained. Using a similar approach as in the four cases above, it is possible to estimate the economic benefits of using the various ammonia sources.

From Table 7-8, at current prices, urea for straw ammoniation has the highest cost, followed by anhydrous ammonia, and the lowest is ammonium carbonate. As urea is a chemical fertilizer in short supply and extensively used in agricultural production, this greatly influences market prices.   Anhydrous ammonia is the raw material for manufacturing urea and ammonium carbonate. Theoretically, it is estimated that 1 t of anhydrous ammonia can manufacture 1.76 t urea or 4.65 t ammonium carbonate, so the cost of ammoniation using anhydrous ammonia should be relatively low.

Table7-8. Cost of different ammonia sources for ammoniating straw

Ammonia source	Ammonia content (%)	Amount used for ammoniation (%)	Price (¥/kg)	Ammoniated straw cost (¥/kg)
Urea	46.67	4.5	1.10	0.050
Anhydrous ammonia	82.35	3.0	1.30	0.039
Ammonium bicarbonate	17.72	10.0	0.30	0.030

NOTE. Only the ammonia source is considered, without the cost of facilities (or equipment). In practice, the equipment cost for ammoniation with anhydrous ammonia is fairly high.

Regardless of the ammonia source for ammoniation, the aim is to improve digestibility and palatability of straw, to supplement with non-protein nitrogen, to improve the protein content of straw and, finally, to replace part of the concentrate. Compared with the price of a predetermined concentrate, the ammonia cost that would make straw ammoniation no longer economic has become a concern of decision-makers. This relates to the upper limit of ammonia cost, which can be calculated by a simple formula:

$$p = a \times b \times x / y$$

Where: p = upper limit of ammonia source cost
a = price of concentrate
b = proportion of ammonia source cost in total cost
x = concentrate saved per unit of ammoniated straw
y = the amount of ammonia used per total DM

A calculation was made using related laboratory data and some published papers. It was assumed that the price of concentrate (a) was ¥ 0.8/kg, and the b value was 0.6. For every kilogram of ammoniated straw, 0.2 kg of concentrate can be saved, therefore $x = 0.2$. Taking the ammonia use per source from Table 7-8, the upper cost limit of every kilogram of ammonia source can be calculated separately.

p_{urea} = 0.8 x 0.6 x 0.2 ÷ 4.5% = ¥ 2.13

$p_{anhydrous\ ammonia}$ = 0.8 x 0.6 x 0.2 ÷ 3% = ¥ 3.2

$p_{ammonium\ bicarbonate}$ = 0.8 x 0.6 x 0.2 ÷ 10% = ¥ 0.96

In the event of exceeding the above upper price limits, from an economic viewpoint it is reasonable to feed more concentrates. In recent years, the price of urea has been below ¥ 1.3/kg. The price of anhydrous ammonia and ammonium bicarbonate are lower than the upper price limits, so the economic benefits are certain.

CASE STUDY ON THE ECONOMICS OF CROP RESIDUES FOR RUMINANTS AT HOUSEHOLD LEVEL

The economic benefits of cattle production based on straw for rural households is influenced by a series of factors, including level of economic development, scale and technology. A comparative analysis has been made on the overall economic benefits and on those of various scales and different feeding technologies in Fuyang Prefecture. There are no grasslands in Fuyang Prefecture, but it markets more beasts than Inner Mongolia. Mengcheng, Lixin and Woyang counties in Fuyang Prefecture constitute the most concentrated area for cattle in China, and are called the Golden Triangle of cattle.

Introduction to the household survey

A survey was conducted in rural households of Mengcheng, Lixin and Guoyang counties, with the objective of analysing and studying cattle production based on straw. The method adopted was random sampling and house-to-house visits. Township and village selection was based on the economic development level and characteristics of cattle production, while the selection of rural households was at random. The time span was from July 1995 to June 1996. From a total of 120 rural households sampled, data from 119 could be obtained (39 in Mengcheng, 40 in Lixin and 40 in Guoyang). The households selected were typical and representative so that the conclusions from the data would be of general and realistic significance.

Situation of straw utilization and the cost of processing and treatment

Straw processing and utilization are the major components of cattle production based on straw. They not only influence the economics of production by rural household every year, but also determine the potential in future years. The results of the survey showed that the average straw output per rural household was 8 624 kg, and the average purchased straw (mainly wheat straw) per household was 997 kg, for a total of 9 622 kg. Among crop residues of different crops, sweet potato vines ranked first, followed by wheat straw and finally maize stover. Their utilization rate was 38.6, 58.4 and 43.2 percent. From the total, ammoniated straws were 17.4 percent, silage 21.4 and direct feeding 47.4, with an average utilization rate of 86.2 percent and a straw treatment utilization rate of 38.8 percent (Table 7-9).

In 1995, Fuyang Prefecture as a whole had achieved a straw utilization rate for cattle production of 64 percent and a straw treatment rate of 18 percent. Although the value was higher than the national average, the trend was similar to the general trend. Compared with a survey conducted in 1993-1994, both the utilization rate and treatment rate had increased. The total straw utilization rate had increased from 76.4 to 86.2 percent.

Table 7-9. Crop residue utilization by rural households (kg)

Straw type	Total	Output	Bought	Treated	Ensiled	Direct feeding	Feeding rate (%)	Treatment rate (%)
Wheat	3 898	3 008	840	1 599	0	1 797	88.3	58.4
Barley	164	164	0	26	0	100	77.1	15.9
Maize	1 996	1 953	43	0	862	492	67.8	43.2
Rice	230	181	49	51	12	158	96.3	27.5
Soybean	323	323	0	2	0	109	49.9	0.6
Sweet potato	3 062	2 996	66	0	1 187	1 855	99.1	38.6
Total	9 622	8 624	998	1 678	2 056	4 560	86.2	38.8

Ammoniating and ensiling were technologies used widely, accounting for 71.4 and 68.1 percent of households interviewed, respectively. The cost of ammoniating and ensiling was the key factor for adoption. Most rural households used a silage-ammoniating pit for treatment, so this method was used for the cost analysis (Table 7-10). In ammoniation, the cost of straw and of urea, the main expenses, accounted for 49.0 and 31.4 percent of total cost, respectively. For ensiling, the main cost was the crop residue itself, 72.7 percent of the total cost.

Table 7-10. Crop residue processing and treatment costs in rural households

Item	Ammoniation	Ensiling
Quantity of crop residue	500 kg	500 kg
Depreciation	¥ 50	¥ 40
Dosage of 4% urea	¥ 40	—
Depreciation	¥ 32	—
Pit cost	¥ 300	¥ 300
Depreciation	¥ 7.5	¥ 7.5
Plastic film cost	¥ 6.5	¥ 4.5
Labour	1 day	0.5 day
Value of labour	¥ 6	¥ 3
Total cost	¥ 102	¥ 55
Average unit cost	¥ 0.204/kg	¥ 0.110/kg

Overall economics at household level

The average number of cattle per household in Fuyang Prefecture was 3.6, with 2.4 marketed and an income from cattle sales of ¥ 3 190 per household. The average total output value was ¥ 5 217 per household. Households used 609.4 kg of grains with a cost of ¥ 806. The average use of concentrate per household was 648.0 kg, with a cost of ¥ 904. The average input volumes were 3 296 kg for common straw, 2 157 kg for silage, 1 991 kg for ammoniated straw and 2 305 kg for green fodder per household, with a total cost of ¥ 1078 for green fodder and roughage. Average annual net output per household was ¥ 2 172, with a net income of ¥ 1 278 and a net earning rate on costs of 32.4 percent. On average, a net earning of ¥ 360 could be obtained for every head of cattle raised; a net earning of ¥ 8.6 and net output value of ¥ 14.6 could be gained for every working day (Table 8-12).

Mengcheng county started earlier and thus it had fairly large-scale cattle production. The average number of cattle per household was 4.2, while in Lixin and Guoyang it was 3.3 cattle. In addition, the feed input type varied among the three counties. The ratio of concentrates:common straw:silage:ammoniated straw was 698:1 284:1 935:1 243 in Mengcheng; 686:1 491:690:1 822 in Lixin; and 721:2 882:809:253 in Guoyang. The concentrate input in the three counties was fairly close, but there was a large difference in straw input type. Mengcheng County had high silage and high ammoniation levels; Lixin County had low silage and high ammoniation; and Guoyang County had low silage, and low ammoniation. For these reasons, the economic benefits of cattle production based on straw in Mengcheng were higher. The average net outputs for cattle production for Mengcheng, Lixin and Guoyang were ¥ 2 448, 2 084 and 1 988; the net incomes were ¥ 1 567, 1 211 and 1 112; and the net earning rate on costs were 34.6, 32.4 and 31.7 percent, respectively. The average net earnings per cattle raised were ¥ 373, 373 and 337; the average net output values per working day were ¥ 16.7, 14.3 and 13.6; and the average net earnings per working day were ¥ 10.7, 8.3 and 7.6 (Table 7-11).

Economics of different feeding scales at household level

In Fuyang Prefecture, more than 50 percent of the rural households had 2-4 head of cattle. Households with 4-6 head were about one third. Households with 1-2 cattle were rare. The average net output with 1-2 cattle was ¥ 738; with 2-4 head it was ¥ 1 621; with 4-6 head it was ¥ 2 563; and with 6-10 head it was ¥ 5 843. The average net earnings from cattle raising for the four groups were ¥ 258, 800, 1 539 and 4 856, and the average net earning rates on costs were 13.8, 25.4, 31.7 and 64.0 percent, respectively. The average net earnings per cattle raised were ¥ 206, 287, 347 and 620; the average net output values per working day were ¥ 9.2, 11.8, 15.0 and 35.5; and the average net earnings per working day were ¥ 3.2, 5.8, 9.0 and 29.5 (Table 7-12).

Economics of different straw treatment techniques

In Fuyang Prefecture, straw processing and treatment techniques generally accepted by rural households included silage and ammoniation. There were four technical combinations of silage and ammoniation: (1) No ensiling, no ammoniation, use of common straw alone; (2) ammoniation without ensiling, plus common straw; (3) only ensiling, without ammoniation, plus common straw; and (4) both ensiling and ammoniation, plus common straw. From the analysis of the survey, it could be seen that cattle production with common straw was the smallest group, and the economic benefits were the lowest. The larger the scale the better the economic benefits. The group of rural households using two techniques at the same time had a larger scale of operation and better economic benefits. The average net output per household of the four groups – (1) common straw; (2) ammoniation; (3) silage; and (4) silage + ammoniation –were respectively ¥ 1 492, 1 748, 2 140 and 2 362; the average net earnings per household were ¥ 581, 886, 1 222 and 1477; the average net earning rate on costs were 20.5, 26.3, 27.4 and 33.2 percent; the average net earnings per cattle raised were ¥ 187, 281, 344 and 381; the average net output values per working day were ¥ 9.8, 12.2, 14.0 and 16.0; and the average net earnings per working day were ¥ 3.8, 6.2, 8.0 and 10.0, respectively (Table 7 13).

The average concentrate input per cattle of the common straw, ammoniation, silage and silage plus ammoniation groups were 262, 308, 508 and 348 kg, respectively. The proportion of common to ammoniated straw per cattle per household in the ammoniation group was 2 198:1 260, while the proportion of common to silage straw per cattle per household was 2 663:1 383 in the silage group. The proportion using treated straw in the ammoniation and silage groups was about 35 percent for both groups. The reason for the gap in economic benefits in both groups was the large input of cottonseed cake in the silage group (an average of 948 kg per household), significantly higher than the other groups. Thus, the economic benefits were very close to those of the silage plus ammoniation group (Table 7-13).

From the rural household survey and the analysis of the production data, it is clear that the economic benefits of cattle production based on straw are significant, and influenced by various inputs, specially concentrates, ammonia source, straw, etc. The economic benefits will change with changes in prices or the cost of all these essential inputs. In order to obtain the best economic benefits, cattle rearers must constantly adjust their diets and feeding methods to match changes in input costs.

Table 7-11. Overall economic benefits of cattle production based on straw by rural households (Units: head, yuan, 500g, working day)

	Average	Mengcheng	Lixin	Guoyang
Number of rural households		39	40	40
Average number of cattle	3.6	4.2	3.3	3.3
Number of cattle marketed	2.4	3.7	2.0	1.6
Income from cattle sales	3 190	4 260	3 119	2 218
Net weight gain	1459	1724	1386	1274
Number of working days per cattle	11.4	10.5	10.4	13.4
Manure output	30 909	34 370	29 307	29 198
Output value of major product	4 639	5 483	4 406	4 051
Output value of sideline products	578	619	535	572
Total output of cattle production	**5 217**	**6 102**	**4 950**	**4 623**
Amount of feed grain used	1 215	1 562	1 195	896
Cost of feed grain	806	1037	802	585
Amount of other concentrates	1 296	13 659	1 036	1 484
Cost of other concentrates	904	894	802	1 016
Amount of common straw	6 593	5 393	4 845	5 910
Cost of common straw	297	243	223	428
Amount of silage used	4 314	8 126	2 241	2 670
Cost of silage	237	447	123	147
Amount of ammoniated straw used	3 981	5 219	5 922	835
Cost of ammoniated straw	406	532	604	85
Amount of green grass used	4 611	6 474	2 298	5 108
Cost of green grass	138	194	69	153
Total amount of green and roughage feed	19 499	25 212	15 306	18 123
Total cost of green grass and roughage	1 078	1 416	1 019	813
Depreciation of shed and other assets	95	97	111	77
Medicines, vaccination, breeding	161	210	131	143
Total cost of materials	**3 045**	**3 654**	**2 865**	**2 635**
Working days	149	147	145	146
Cost of labour	895	881	873	876
Total cost of production	**3 940**	**4 535**	**3 738**	**3 111**
Net output from cattle production	2 173	2 448	2 084	1 988
Net earning from cattle production	1 278	2 567	1 211	1 112
Net earning rate on costs	32.4	34.6	32.4	31.7
Net earning per cattle	359.9	373.0	372.6	337.1
Net output value per working day	14.6	16.7	14.3	13.6
Net earnings per working day	8.6	10.7	8.3	7.6

Table7-12. Overall economic benefits of cattle production under different cattle numbers by rural households (Units: cattle, yuan, 500 g, working day)

Group (number of cattle/household)	1-2	2-44	4-6	6-10
Number of rural households	6	69	35	9
Average cattle number	1.3	2.8	4.4	7.8
Number of cattle marketed whole period	1.3	1.4	2.6	9.9
Income from cattle sales	1 127	2 014	3 865	10 957
Net weight gain	577	1 093	1 782	3 596
Number of working days per cattle	2.6	11.0	14.0	10.6
Manure output	18 031	23 975	30 339	59 876
Output value of major product	1 834	3 477	5 666	11 434
Output value of sideline products	296	470	730	1 004
Total output of cattle production	**2 130**	**3 947**	**6 395**	**12 438**
Amount of feed grain used	435	859	1 556	3 176
Cost of feed grain	285	569	1 027	2 117
Amount of other concentrate	673	971	1 809	2 205
Cost of other concentrate feed	442	672	1 284	1 515
Amount of common straw	4 040	6 330	7 211	7 905
Cost of common straw	181.79	284.86	324.47	355.73
Amount of silage used	2 042	2 539	539	15 067
Cost of silage	112	140	299	829
Amount of ammoniated straw used	1 843	2 868	4 681	11 224
Cost of ammoniated straw	188	293	477	1 145
Amount of green grass used	1 830	4 522	4 618	7 120
Cost of green grass	55	136	139	214
Total amount of green and roughage feed	9 755	16 258	21 949	41 316
Total cost of green grass and roughage	537	853	1 240	2 543
Depreciation of shed and other assets	85	95	90	118
Medicines, vaccines, breeding expenses	44	137	191	302
Total cost of materials	**1 393**	**2 326**	**3 832**	**6 595**
Working days	79	137	171	165
Cost of labour	479	821	1 024	988
Total cost of production	**1 872**	**3 147**	**4 856**	**7 583**
Net output from cattle production	737	1 621	2 564	5 843
Net earning from cattle production	258	800	1 540	4 855
Net earning rate on costs	13.8	25.4	31.7	64.0
Net earning per cattle	206.2	286.6	346.7	620.0
Net output value per working day	9.2	11.8	15.0	35.5
Net earnings per working day	3.2	5.8	9.0	29.5

Economic analysis of animal production based on crop resides

Table 7-13. Overall economic benefits of cattle production based on straw under with different feeding techniques by rural households (Units: cattle, yuan, 500 g, working days)

Technical type group	Common straw	Ammoniation	Silage	Silage and ammoniation
Number of rural households	21	17	13	68
Average cattle number	3.1	3.2	3.6	3.9
Number of cattle marketed	0.7	2.2	2.1	3.0
Income from cattle sales	942	3 045	3 093	3 970
Net weight gain	926	1 158	1 605	1 671
Numbers of working days per cattle	13.1	12.6	12.1	11.0
Manure output	22 720	29 959	30 227	33 162
Output value of major product	2 944	3 684	5 103	5 313
Output value of sideline products	471	575	574	607
Total output of cattle production	**3 415**	**4 259**	**6 577**	**5 921**
Amount of feed grain used	697	894	1 210	1 432
Cost of feed grain	453	604	800	952
Amount of other concentrates	929	1 046	2 398	1 268
Cost of other concentrates	634	782	1 640	885
Amount of common straw	9 429	6 923	9 452	4 960
Cost of common straw	424	311	425	223
Amount of silage used	0	0	4 910	6 585
Cost of silage	0	0	270	362
Amount of ammoniated straw used	0	3 969	0	5 975
Cost of ammoniated straw	0	405	0	609
Amount of green grass used	7 698	4 685	3 930	8 475
Cost of green grass	231	141	118	254
Total of green and roughage feed	14 048	15 578	18 292	25 995
Total cost of green grass and roughage	655	857	813	1 449
Depreciation of shed and other assets	64.1	104.1	114.6	99.6
Medicines, vaccines, breeding	116.3	162.8	170.0	173.2
Total cost of materials	**1 923**	**2 511**	**3 538**	**3 559**
Working days	152	144	153	147
Cost of labour	912	862	917	884
Total cost of production	**2 834**	**3 373**	**4 455**	**4 443**
Net output from cattle production	1 492	1 748	2 140	2 362
Net earning from cattle production	581	886	1 222	1 477
Net earning rate on costs	20.5	26.3	27.4	33.2
Net earning per cattle	187.4	281.2	344.4	380.7
Net output value per working day	9.8	12.2	14.0	16.0
Net earnings per working day	3.8	6.2	8.0	10.0

Chapter 8

The future challenge

Guo Tingshuang
Ministry of Agriculture, PRC

In 1992, the *Animal Production based on Crop Residues* (APCR) project was listed in the State Agricultural Comprehensive Development Programme (SACDP) of China. In only nine years, 13 state-level APCR prefectures and 380 APCR demonstration counties had been established, and more than 8 million farmer households were utilizing ammoniated straw to raise livestock. The implementation of the APCR project not only enabled severalfold increases in beef, mutton and milk production, but also saved more than 50 million tonne of feed grain annually. Thereby, China reduced its grain imports, making a contribution towards world grain security. The APCR project has driven the development of slaughtering and processing of meat, leather, horns, bones, blood, etc. This, together with the sale of these products, has provided employment for 20 million people in rural and urban areas, making a contribution to farmer income and maintaining social stability. The return of manure to farmland in the APCR not only improved soil and agriculture outputs, but also reduced chemical fertilizer use and its environmental pollution, thereby reducing the generation of "red tides" and other ecological calamities. The effective utilization of crop residues also diminished air pollution caused by annual straw burning. Implementation of the APCR project in the past decade has not only generated over ¥ 70 000 million in direct economic benefits, but also generated favourable social, agronomic and environmental benefits.

Although the APCR project has already had great achievements, looking into the future, the burden is heavy and the way is still long. Strategically, Chinese agriculture confronts multiple challenges, and the situation is serious. The first challenge is population growth. China has a population of 1 300 million (22 percent of the world) that will grow by more than 14 million a year. This increase will demand at least 5.6 million tonne of food grain. However, in the past 16 years, annual grain output increased only by 4.5 million tonne. The second challenge is the pressure coming from higher living standard since, together with economic development, the consumption of meat, eggs, milk and fish is continuously increasing. This means extra feed grain to produce them. The third challenge is continuous reduction in farmland area, worsening ecological conditions. The development of the economy requires the constructing of highways, factories, commercial centres and domestic accommodation, which occupy large areas of former farmland. In merely the last three years (1996-1999), net reduction in farmland was 13 million *mu*, equivalent to the land of 10 counties. At the same time, due to natural and mainly anthropogenic calamities, annual deterioration of pasture land has exceeded 10 million *mu*. This continuous environmental deterioration is fundamentally destroying the base for agricultural production. Most domestic and foreign scholars have predicted than in 2-3 decades, China will need to import huge amounts of grain to meet the continually rising demand. However, the grain that can be provided worldwide is also limited. If a great country with 1 300 million population imports large grain amounts, it will certainly threaten world grain security.

To solve the grain problem, "tapping new resources and economizing on expenditure" has been proposed. The "tapping new resources" implies "increasing output." If enough grain is produced, the problem is solved. But history shows that in the last 16 years grain output increases in China could not keep up with population growth. Facing this situation, the only way out is "economize on expenditure."

As mentioned before, through implementation of the APCR project, there have been annual savings in feed grain equivalent to over 50 million tonne. This is far from the maximum limit. So far, from the over 600 million tonne of crop residues annually, only about 200 million tonne are used as feed, of which less than half is treated (silage, ammoniation, etc.). Its further exploitation still has great potential. Nevertheless, crop residues can only be fed to herbivorous animals, not to swine or poultry. Only by making a great effort in developing herbivore production will full utilization of crop residues be possible. In China, herbivorous animals are a relatively weak element of the livestock industry. Beef, mutton, milk, leather, hair and feathers are all in short supply. MOA recently formulated a policy guide for animal production restructuring, namely: "stabilize pork and poultry egg production; raise beef, mutton and poultry meat production; and intensively develop milk, quality wool and fine hair production." In other words, strive to develop herbivorous animal production.

In the first chapter it was already demonstrated that, in China, the main base for the development of herbivorous animals is the agricultural zone, the basic feed being crop residues and other crop by-products. State Council leaders have already decided that the APCR project ought to be unremittingly carried out. Therefore, MOA has already formulated a *National development scheme for a project on animal production based on crop residues 2001-2010* (henceforth called the Scheme), planning APCR work for the next decade.

According to the Scheme, in the coming 10 years, apart from consolidating the 13 current, 47 additional demonstration prefectures ought to be established. According to the State Great Development Strategy for West China, the new demonstration prefectures and counties should be towards west China, since, in the past, most were in the Central Plain and in east China. Establishment of APCR demonstration counties in the cropping and pastoral mixed zone combines animal raising based on grass and APCR. Using a confined system instead of grazing allows for the rehabilitation of grasslands, striving for a dual goal: animal production and ecological reconstruction. Besides, the new Scheme stipulates that demonstration prefectures and counties ought to implement the guiding policy of paying equal attention to new settings and extension, and respect regional development. This consolidates the existing extension base, gradually constituting a recognized production pattern.

If Scheme targets are reached, crop residues for animal raising should reach 385 million tonne by 2010, equivalent to 55 percent of all crop residues. Of this, silage will be 250 million tonne (fresh weight) and ammoniated residues 120 million tonne. Feed grain saved will equal 126 million tonne (62 million tonne in the next decade), which will compensate for the grain demand from population growth in this period. In addition, APCR will make huge contributions to social employment, to development of ecological agriculture and to environmental protection. The full text of the Scheme annexed to this publication.

Plate 8-1. Dr R. Orskov, a FAO expert, in China

Plate 8-2. State Councillor Mr Chen Junsheng inspects a beef cattle slaughter
house

Plate 8-3. Yellow Cattle competition - the champion

Plate 8-4. Developing the beef cattle feed-lot

Lapierre, C., Monties, B., & Rolando, C. 1988. Thioacidolysis of diazomethane-methylated pine compression wood and wheat straw *in situ* lignins. *Holzforschung*, **42**:409-411.

Lawton, E.J., Bellamy, W.D., Hungate, R.E., Bryant, M.P., & Hall, E. 1951. Some effects of high velocity electrons on wood. *Science*, **113**:380-382.

Li, S.D., & Wu, J.Q. 1991. Productive performance of dairy cows given on anhydrous ammonia-treated rice straw. *China Dairy Cattle,* **9**(3):47-48.

Li, D.F., Qiao, S.Y., Zhang, X.M., & Zhu, X.P. 1995. Current situation in manufacture and utilization of urea-molasses lick blocks in China. *China Feed*, **17**:2-4.

Li,Y., Gu, C.X., Cao, Y.F., Liu, R.C., & Li, J.G. 1998. Relationship between intake and degradability of forages, and their associate effect. *In: Proceedings of the 3rd National Symposium on Feed Sciences and Animal Nutrition*. Chengdu, Sichuan, China, 28-31 October 1998. China Society of Animal Nutrition, Beijing.

Lie, D.A. 1975. Report on straw utilization. Presented at Internordisk Halmmote, Sundsvollen, 1975. Agricultural Research Council, Norway.

Liu, J.C., Pan, T.G., Su, S.J., Lin, J.R., & Ke, Y.Q. 1998. Replacement of wheat bran with mushroom substrate residues in growing pig diets. *Chinese J. Anim. Sci.,* **34**(2):26-27.

Liu, J.X. 1995. Supplementation of low quality crop residue. p.165-180, *in:* F. Dolberg and P.E. Petersen (eds). *Agricultural Science for Biodiversity and Sustainability in Developing Countries.* Proceeding of a Workshop held at Tune Landboskole, Denmark, April 1995.

Liu, J.X., Chen, Z.M., Yu, J.Q., Fei, B.R., Wang, W.D., & Zhang, J.F. 1998. Effects of ammonium bicarbonate treatment and rape seed meal supplementation on growth performance in Huzhou lambs receiving rice straw. *Livest. Res. Rural Dev.,* **10**(2):Paper 3.

Liu, J.X., Wang, X.Q., Shi, Q.Z., & Ye, H.W. 2000. Nutritional evaluation of bamboo shoot shell and its effect as supplementary feed on performance of heifer offered ammoniated rice straw diet. *Asian-Aus. J. Anim. Sci.*, **13**(10):1388-1393.

Liu, J.X., Wu, Y.M., Xu, N.Y., & Wu, Z.W. 1993. Efficiency of protein utilisation of formaldehyde treated rapeseed meal by sheep and its influence on cattle's performance. *Asian-Aus. J. Anim. Sci.*, **6**(4):601-605.

Liu, J.X., Wu, Y.M., Zhu, S.Q., & Xu, Z.Y. 1994. Comparative efficiency of utilization of nitrogen of formaldehyde-treated rapeseed meal and soybean meal in ammoniated rice straw diet by Hu Sheep. *China Anim. Sci.*, **1**(1):12-19.

Liu, J.X., Wu, Y.M., Dai, X.M., Jun Yao, Zhou, Y.Y., & Chen, Y.J. 1995. The effects of urea-mineral lick blocks on the liveweight gain of local yellow cattle and goats in grazing conditions. *Liv. Res. Rural Dev.*, **7**(2): 9-13.

Liu, J.X., Wu, Y.M., Dai, X.M., Tong, Q.X., Cai, G., & Lin, C.Y. 1991a. Performance of growing heifers fed on ammonia bicarbonate-treated rice straw. *China Dairy Cattle*, **1**:29-30.

Liu, J.X., Xu, N.Y., Wu, Y.M., Dai, X.M., Zhang, Z.D., Yang, H., Xia, F.T., Wu, J.P., & Ni, Y.J. 1991b. Study on improving the feed value of straw by treatment with ammonia. 3. Milk yield of lactating cows receiving ammonium bicarbonate treated rice straw. *Zhejiang J. Anim. Sci. Vet. Med.*, **16**(3): 2-6.

Liu, J.X., Xu, N.Y., Wu, Y.M., Yang, H., & Zhang, Z.D. 1992. Performance of heifers and lactating cows offered ammonium bicarbonate treated rice straw. (Abstract) p.412, *in: Proceedings of 6th Conference of National Society of Animal Nutrition*, CAASV.

Liu, J.X., Yao, J., Yan, B., Yu, J.Q., Shi, Z.Q., & Yao, J. 2001. Effects of mulberry leaves to replace rapeseed meal on performance of sheep feeding on ammoniated straw diet. *Small Ruminant Research*, **39**(2): 131-136.

Liu, J.X., Ye, J.A., & Ye, H.W. 1997. Effects of supplementary Chinese milk vetch silage on straw intake and growth rate of Holstein heifers given ammoniated rice straw. *Anim. Feed Sci. Technol.*, **65**: 78-86.

Lu, D.L., Huang, Y.Y., Ma, Y., Yang, R.Z., Nu, N., Cheng, C.H., & Liu, L.J. 1984. Ammoniation of rice straw and its feeding value for dairy cattle. *Xinjiang Agric. Sci.*, **6**:39-41.

Lu Ming. 1998. Do a good job in integrated utilization of straws by strictly prohibiting burning straw. MOA document.

Lu Xilei. 1991. Ammonia treated straw for dairy cows. Unpublished report.

Lu, X.Y., & Wang, G.Q. 1990. Effectiveness of addition of cellulolytic enzymes to dairy cow diets. *Heilongjiang J. Anim. Sci. Vet. Med.*, **10**:12.

Lu, Z.X., & Xiong, C.R. 1991. Glucose release from rice straw treated with combination of electron irradiation and sodium hydroxide. *Jiangsu J. Agric. Sci.*, **7**(2):27-31.

Lu, Y., Yang, B.Y., Guan, Y.Y., Huang, F., Fang, W.Y., & Tang, X.F. 1995a. Preliminary study on urea-molasses blocks for growing buffaloes. *Guangxi J. Anim. Husb. Vet. Med.*, **11**(4):24-25.

Lu, Z.Z., Yang, H., Yang, S.H., & Dong, Q.L. 1995b. Effect of various levels of mushroom substrate residues in pig diets on their growth performance. *Chinese J. Anim. Sci.*, **31**(6):34.

Ma, Y.S., & Zhu, G.S. 1997. Comparison of ammoniation and silage fermentation of corn stovers and feeding lactating cows. *China Dairy Cattle,* **2**: 26-27.

Ma, S., Dong, D.K., Chen, C.X., Xu, S.C., & Chen, Q.G. 1989. Study on feeding of ammoniated wheat straw to steers. *Qinghai J. Anim. Sci. & Vet. Med.,* 1989(3):13-15.

Ma, T.K., Gu, C.X., Dai, B.C., & Orskov, E.R. 1990. Effect of ammonia treatment of wheat and level of concentrate on performance of Chinese Yellow Cattle. *Livestock Research and Rural Development*, **2**(3):49-53.

Ma, W.H., Han, S.J., Wang, D.C., Wang, L.H., Liu, C., & Chen, L.X. 1995. Effect of NPN-containing lick blocks on fattening performance of beef cattle. *China Feed*, **15**:23.

Ma, Y.Z., Ti, X.Y., Zhen, R.L., & Xu, J.Y. 1992. Manufacturing and evaluation
   of molasses-urea lick block. *Tianjin Agricultural Sciences,* **1**:25-26.

Mao, H.M., & Feng, Y.L. 1991. Treatment of crop residues with combination of
   urea and calcium hydroxide to improve their nutritional value. *Chinese J.
   Anim. Sci.,* **27**(5):3-5.

Meng, Q.X.. 1988. Ammoniation conditions of crop residues and the maximized
   utilization of ammonia-treated wheat straw in the feeding system of
   growing and finishing ruminants. Ph.D Dissertation. Beijing Agricultural
   University, China.

Meng, Q.X. 1990. Upgrading utilization of roughage including crop residues in
   ruminant production. *Hebei J. Anim. Sci. Vet. Med.,* **1**:52-55.

Meng, Q.X., & Xiong, Y.Q. 1990. The effect of treatment of wheat straw by
   irradiation combined with chemicals on its nutritive value. *J. Nuclear-
   Agric. Sci.,* **11**:270-274.

Meng, Q.X. & Xiong, Y.Q. 1993. Effects of ammonia treatment and concentrate
   supplementation on growth performance in Wuzhumuqin wethers receiving
   wheat straw. *Acta Vetrinaria et Zootechnica Sinica,* **24**(1):23-28.

Meng, Q.X., Xiao, X.J., Yu, H., Zhou, W.S., & Qiao, Z.G. 1999. Treatment of
   wheat straw with microorganisms and the nutritive value of treated straw
   as feeds for growing beef cattle. *Chinese J. Anim. Sci.,* **35**(6):3-5.

Meng, Q.X., Xiong, Y.Q., Jiang, H.M., & Xu, L.J. 1990a. Use of ammoniated
   wheat straw in growing and finishing beef cattle. *Chinese J. Anim. Sci.,*
   26(6):8-11.

Meng, Q.X., Xiong, Y.Q., Li, Y.R., Ji J.Q., & Wang, S.L. 1990b. Computer
   simulation for optimizing beef cattle feeding on ammoniated straw diets.
   Acta Agriculturae Universitatis Pekinensis, **16**(4):437-441.

Minson, D.J. 1990. *Forage in Ruminant Nutrition.* New York, NY: Academic
   Press.

MOA [Ministry of Agriculture]. 1990. Safety operation regulations for straw
   ammoniation.

Nedkvitne, J.J., & Maurtvedt. A. 1980. Ammoniakkbehandla, torrluta (NaOH) og resirkulasjonaluta halm som for til sauer. p.411-416, *in:* [Proceedings of] Husdyrforsoksmotet. Agricultural University of Norway.

O'Neill, N., Albersheim, P., & Darvill, A. 1990. The pectic polysaccharides of primary cell walls. p.415-441, *in:* P.M. Dey and J.B. Harborne (eds) *Methods in Plant Biochemistry.* Vol. 2. *Carbohydrates.* London: Academic Press.

Ørskov, E.R. 1987. Treated straw for ruminants. *Res. Dev. Agric.*, **4**(2):65-69.

Peng, J. 1998. Activities of cellulolytic enzymes and ligninase before and after treatment of wheat straw with White Rot fungi. Undergraduate student thesis, China Agric. Univ.

Preston, T.R., & Leng, R.A. 1984. Supplementation of diets based on fibrous residues and by-products. p.373-413, *in:* F. Sundstol and E. Owen (eds). *Straw and Other Fibrous By-products as Feeds.* Amsterdam: The Netherlands: Elsevier.

Preston, T.R. 1995. Tropical Animal Feeding. A manual for research workers. *FAO Animal Production and Health Paper*, No. 126.

Pritchard, G.I., Pigden, W.J., & Minton, D.J. 1962. Effect of gamma radiation on the utilization of wheat straw by rumen microorganisms. *Can. J. Anim. Sci.*, **42**:215-217.

Sansoucy, R. 1995. New developments in the manufacturing and utilization of multinutrient block. *World Animal Review*, **82**(1):78-83.

Shi, C.L. 1998. Initial report on feeding beef cattle with corn stovers treated with combination of sodium hydroxide and urea. *Feed Panorama*, **10**(5):4.

Shi, Z.Q., Wang, X.Q., Liu, J.X., & Ye, H.W. 1997. Effect of supplementing with ammoniated straw on growth performance of heifers offered rice straw. *China Feed*, **1**:17-18.

Song, X.C., Zhang, L.J., Ma, Y., Chang, F., Wang, X.C., & Li, X.B. 1998. Response of lactation to ammoniation of wheat straw in high yield dairy cattle. *China Dairy Cattle*, **2**:28-29.

Su Hui, Wu Minglou, Fang Bichun, Zong Shengyin, & Su Zhanjun. 1997. A great improvement in milk yield resulting from feeding diets with addition of cellulose enzyme products. *China Dairy Cattle,* **3**:25-26.

Sun, Q.H. 1985. Alkali treated wheat straw for beef cattle. *Feed Research,* **5**:15-16.

Sun, Z.Y., Chen, Y.J., Yang, Y., & Deng, Z.Y. 1991. Feeding dairy cattle with scrubbed soybean straw. *Heilongjiang J. Anim. Sci. Vet. Med.,* **10**:20.

Sundstol, F., & Ekeern, A. 1982. Energy metabolism of farm animals. EAAP Publication No.29: 120-123.

Sundstol, F., & Owen, E. 1984. *Straw and Other Fibrous By-products as Feed.* Amsterdam, The Netherlands: Elsevier

Sundstol, F., Coxworth,, E., & Mowat, D.N. 1978. Improving the nutritive value of straw and other low-quality roughages by treatment with ammonia. *World Animal Review,* **26**:13-21.

Sundstol, F., Said, N., & Arnason, J. 1979. Factors influencing the effect of chemical treatment on the nutritive value of straw. *Acta Agric. Scand.,* **29**:179-190.

Van Soest, P.J. 1994. *Nutritional Ecology of the Ruminant.* Ithaca, NY: Cornell University Press.

Wang, A. 1998. Studies on dietary application of cellulose complex in monogastric and ruminant animals. *J. Northeast Agric. Univ.,* **29**(3):236-251.

Wang, X.C., Li, X.B., & Pi, B. 1996. Combination treatment of wheat straw with ammoniation and ensilage and feeding treated straw to lactation cows. *Heilongjiang J. Anim. Sci. Vet. Med.,* **7**:20-21.

Wang, X.L., Lin, Z.Y., Sun, Z.X., & Song, Y.H. 1995. Effect of multinutrient lick blocks on performance of dairy cows. *Liaoning J. Anim. Husb. Vet. Med.,* **5**:10-11.

Wang, X.Q. 1997. Evaluation of bamboo shoot shell as a supplementary feed to ruminants on ammonium bicarbonate treated rice straw based diets. M.Sc. Thesis. Zhejiang Agricultural University, China.

Wu, K.Q. 1996. Research report of feeding microbial ensiled wheat straw to beef cattle. *Chinese J. Cattle Sci.*, **22**(Suppl.):34-37.

Xia, J.P., Xie, M., Han, L.J., Lu, T.K., & Fan, X.M. 1994. Manufacturing of equipment set for production of molasses-urea lick blocks. *J. Beijing Agric. Engineer. Univ.*, **14**(2):60-63.

Xiao, X.J. 1998. Chemical composition and *in vitro* digestibility of wheat straw before and after treatment with white rot fungi. Undergraduate student thesis, China Agricultural University.

Xing, Tingxian. 1995. *Nutrition value and utilization of crop residues.* Changsha, China: Hunan Science and Technology Press.

Xiong, Y.Q. 1986. Processing and treatment of crop residues and the utilization of treated residues in ruminant feeding. *Chinese J. Anim. Sci.*, **22**(2):21-23.

Xu, L.Q. 1989. Investigation on effect of feeding ammoniated wheat straw on performance of beef cattle. Collection of papers on integrated development of agriculture. Beijing Academy of Agricultural Sciences. Beijing.

Xu, Q.L., Zhao, Y.B., & Lin, Q. 1993. Trial on milk enhancer – urea molasses lick block for dairy cattle. *Qinghai J. Anim. Husb. Vet. Med.*, **26**(6):1-2.

Xu, Z.C., Tian, Y.J., & Wang, H. 1994. Performance of goats and sheep supplemented with multinutrient lick blocks. *Sichuan Anim. Sci. and Vet. Med.*, No.3:27-29.

Yang, X.Y., Cao, Q., & Zhu, M.Z. 1986. Substrate residues from mushroom culture as feed ingredient for pigs. (Abstract) p.98-99, *in: Proceedings of 4th Conference of National Society of Animal Nutrition*, CAASV.

Yang, Y.F., Jiang, Y., & Wen, J. 1996. Manufacture of multimineral lick blocks and its effect on sheep. *Feed Outlook*, **8**(3):7-8.

Ye, R.S., Hong, R.L., & Zhu, Y.H. 1999. Report on use of alkali-treated rice straw in dairy cow diets. *China Dairy Cattle*, **2**:28-29.

Ye, J.A., Liu, J.X., & Yao, J. 1996. The effect of ammoniated rice straw diets supplemented with Chinese milk vetch silage on rumen fermentation and microflora in sheep. *Livest. Res. Rural Dev.*, **8**(4):45-52.

Zhang, L.J., Song, X.C., Ma, Y., & Wang, J.H. 1995. Feeding ammoniated corn stovers to lactating dairy cows. *China Dairy Cattle*, **1**:22-23.

Zhang, T.Z., Zhang, J.G., Wang, D.C., & Liu, F.R. 1982. Summary on studies of ammoniation of crop residues. *Liaoning J. Anim. Sci. Vet. Med.*, **5**:17-21.

Zhang, Y., & Meng, D.L. 1995. Use of microbial ensiled wheat straw to feed dairy cattle. *China Dairy Cattle*, **6**:18-19.

Zhang, Z.W., Zhang, X.M., Li, D.F., & Liu, J.W. 1993. Investigation on growth performance of beef steers supplemented with multinutrient lick blocks containing NPN. *Feed Industry*, **14**(8):34-35.

Zhang, B., Li, L.L., Liu, C.Y., Lin, D.M., Chen, G.W., & Huang, C.L. 1999. Effect of multinutrient lick blocks on performance of growing goats. *Animal Ecology*, **20**(2):4-8.

Zhao, C.Y. 1999. Cellulose byproducts can be used as a good source of ruminant animals. *China Feed*, **19**:26.

Zhao, K.P., & Huo, Q.G. 1990. Investigation on performance of growing heifers offered ammoniated rice straw. *China Dairy Cattle*, **8**(1):28-29.

Zhao, X.Y., & Sun, Q.L. 1992. Feeding kneaded corn stovers to dairy cattle. *China Dairy Cattle*, **4**:20.

Zhou, M.Q. 1994. Requirement for re-consideration of traditional pig-feeding system on family farms in rural areas of China. p.309-320, *in:* Z.Y. Zhang (ed). *Recent Advances in Animal Nutrition in China*. Beijing: China Agriculture Publishing House.

Zhou, Z.W. 1991. Response of growth performance to addition of mushroom substrate residues in pig diets. *Chinese J. Anim. Sci.*, **27**(2):42-47.